Tim A. Osswald

Polymer Processing Fundamentals

Hanser Publishers, Munich

Hanser/Gardner Publications, Inc., Cincinnati

The Author:
Tim A. Osswald, University of Wisconsin-Madison, Polymer Research Group,
Department of Mechanical Engineering, Madison, WI 53706, USA

Distributed in the USA and in Canada by
Hanser/Gardner Publications, Inc.
6915 Valley Avenue, Cincinnati, Ohio 45244-3029, USA
Fax: (513) 527-8950
Phone: (513) 527-8977 or 1-800-950-8977
Internet: http://www.hansergardner.com

Distributed in all other countries by
Carl Hanser Verlag
Postfach 86 04 20, 81631 München, Germany
Fax: +49 (89) 98 12 64

The use of general descriptive names, trademarks, etc., in this publication, even if the former are not
especially identified, is not to be taken as a sign that such names, as understood by the Trade Marks
and Merchandise Marks Act, may accordingly be used freely by anyone.

While the advice and information in this book are believed to be true and accurate at the date of going
to press, neither the authors nor the editors nor the publisher can accept any legal responsibility for
any errors or omissions that may be made. The publisher makes no warranty, express or implied, with
respect to the material contained herein.

Library of Congress Cataloging-in-Publication Data
Osswald, Tim A.
Polymer processing fundamentals / Tim A. Osswald.
     p.   cm.
Includes bibliographical references and index.
ISBN 1-56990-262-3 (pbk.)
1. Plastics.   I. Title.
TP1120.D85   1998
668.4–dc21   98-33644

Die Deutsche Bibliothek – CIP-Einheitsaufnahme
Osswald, Tim A.
Polymer processing fundamentals / Tim A. Osswald. – Munich :
Hanser ; Cincinnati : Hanser/Gardner, 1998
     ISBN 3-446-19571-8

© Carl Hanser Verlag, Munich 1998
Camera-ready copy prepared by the author
Printed and bound in Germany by Druckhaus "Thomas Müntzer", Bad Langensalza

In loving memory of Max Robert Osswald

Foreword

The Society of Plastics Engineers is pleased to sponsor and endorse "Polymer Processing Fundamentals" by Tim Osswald. This volume is extremely well written and structured. The comprehensive text makes it an excellent resource for students and engineers. The author's writing style and knowledge of the subject matter have resulted in a competent, well-balanced presentation.

SPE, through its Technical Volumes Committee, has long sponsored books on various aspects of plastics. Its involvement has ranged from identification of needed volumes and recruitment of authors to peer review and approval and publication of new books.

Technical competence pervades all SPE activities, not only in the publication of the books, but also in other areas such as sponsorship of technical conferences and educational programs. In addition, the Society publishes periodicals including *Plastics Engineering, Polymer Engineering and Science, The Journal of Injection Molding Technology, Journal of Vinyl & Additive Technology* and *Polymer Composites* as well as conference proceedings and other publications, all of which are subject to rigorous technical review procedures.

The resource of some 38,000 practicing plastics engineers, scientists, and technologists has made SPE the largest organization of its type worldwide. Further information is available from the Society at 14 Fairfield Drive, Brookfield, Connecticut 06804, USA.

Michael R. Cappelletti
Executive Director
Society of Plastics Engineers

Technical Volumes Committee
Robert C. Portnoy, Chairperson
Exxon Chemical Company

Dan Weissman, Reviewer
Schmalbach Lubeca

Preface

This book provides some background on polymer processing to engineering students and practicing engineers. It is written at two levels: an introductory level for students and engineers unfamiliar with polymer processing, and a more advanced level for more in-depth material. The more advanced material is shaded to distinguished it from the introductory level. The book presents enough information so that, with their fluids and heat transfer background, engineers can understand and solve polymer processing problems.

Polymer Processing Fundamentals is based on lecture notes from a five-week polymer processing laboratory course taught at the University of Wisconsin-Madison. The introductory level of this book is currently being used in this course.

The first three chapters cover general topics such as historical background, molecular structure of polymers, thermal properties of polymers, mechanical behavior of polymers, and polymer rheology. Chapters 4 through 8 cover the most important polymer processes. Chapter 4 is dedicated to extrusion, Chapter 5 to mixing and Chapter 6 to injection molding. Secondary shaping such as film blowing, film casting, blow molding, and thermoforming is detailed in Chapter 7. The last chapter covers other processes such as calendering, coating, compression molding, foaming, and rotational molding. Laboratory exercises on extrusion, injection molding, blow molding, thermoforming, and film blowing are presented at the end of the book.

I cannot possibly acknowledge everyone who helped in the preparation of this manuscript. First, I would like to thank all the students of my polymer processing course who, in the past few years, have endured my experimenting with new ideas. I am also grateful to my polymer processing colleagues who taught the course before me: Ronald L. Daggett, a true polymer processing pioneer, who had enough vision to include plastics and plastics processing in the mechanical engineering curriculum at the University of Wisconsin-Madison in 1946; the late Lew Erwin, who greatly contributed to the field of mixing, and who continued Daggett's quest; and Jeroen Rietveld who completely renovated the polymer processing laboratories in the early 90s and developed the laboratories presented in this book. Special thanks are due to A. Jeffrey Giacomin for reviewing and proofreading the entire manuscript, and for serving as a sounding board during the preparation of the book. Bruce Davis, Paul Gramann, Antoine Rios, and Richard Theriault I thank for proofreading and giving constructive suggestions. I thank Daniel Feiler for preparing the camera-ready manuscript and for the superb job in drawing most of the figures. Daniel Feiler and Lynda Litzkow are acknowledged for helping with the cover design. I am grateful to Lian Zhao for developing the film blowing laboratory, and to Maria del Pilar Noriega of the ICIPC in Medellin, Colombia, for the extrusion laboratory data. Special thanks to Wolfgang Cohnen for the photograph of Nestles Canyon used in Chapter 3. I am grateful to Wolfgang Glenz, Ed Immergut, Martha Kürzl, and Christine Strohm of Hanser Publishers for their support throughout the book's development, and to Thea Teich for copyediting the final manuscript. Above all, I thank my wife Diane, and my children Palitos and Rudi for everything.

Tim A. Osswald

Table of Contents

1 Introduction to Polymers 1

    1.1   Historical Background 1
    1.2   General Properties 3
    1.3   Macromolecular Structure of Polymers.......................7
    1.4   Molecular Weight..9
    1.5   Arrangement of Polymer Molecules........................11
           1.5.1   Thermoplastic Polymers.........................11
           1.5.2   Amorphous Thermoplastics.....................11
           1.5.3   Semi-Crystalline Thermoplastics...............12
           1.5.4   Thermosets 13
    1.6   Copolymers and Polymer Blends.............................14
    1.7   Polymer Additives..15
           1.7.1   Plasticizers.......................................15
           1.7.2   Flame Retardants.................................15
           1.7.3   Stabilizers..16
           1.7.4   Antistatic Agents 16
           1.7.5   Fillers...16
           1.7.6   Blowing Agents 17
    Examples...17
    Problems...18
    References...18

2 Mechanical Behavior of Polymers 19

    2.1   Viscoelastic Behavior of Polymers..........................19
           2.1.1   Stress Relaxation 19
           2.1.2   Time-Temperature Superposition...............20
    2.2   The Short-Term Tensile Test..................................22
           2.2.1   Elastomers..23
           2.2.2   Thermoplastic Polymers.........................25
    2.3   Long-Term Tests...26
           2.3.1   Isochronous and Isometric Creep Plots 27
           2.3.2   Creep Rupture 29
    2.4   Dynamic Mechanical Tests....................................29
    2.5   Mechanical Behavior of Filled and Reinforced Polymers...........32
    2.6   Impact Strength 36
    2.7   Fatigue...38
    2.8   Weathering..40
    Examples...41
    Problems...43

References...45

3   Rheology of Polymer Melts...47

    3.1   Introduction to Rheology..47
        3.1.1   Shear Thinning Behavior of Polymers.....................48
        3.1.2   Normal Stresses in Shear Flow................................52
        3.1.3   Deborah Number...54
        3.1.4   Rheology of Curing Thermosets 56
        3.1.5   Suspension Rheology 57
    3.2   Rheometry...59
        3.2.1   The Melt Flow Indexer...60
        3.2.2   The Capillary Viscometer 60
        3.2.3   The Cone-and-Plate Rheometer 63
    Examples..64
    Problems...65
    References..65

4   Extrusion...67

    4.1   The Plasticating Extruder...69
        4.1.1   The Solids Conveying Zone......................................72
        4.1.2   The Melting Zone 76
        4.1.3   The Metering Zone 79
    4.2   Extrusion Dies..81
        4.2.1   Sheeting Dies 82
        4.2.2   Tubular Dies 84
    Examples..85
    Problems...91
    References..93

5   Mixing..95

    5.1   Distributive Mixing..95
        5.1.1   Effect of Orientation 96
    5.2   Dispersive Mixing..99
        5.2.1   Break-Up of Particulate Agglomerates 99
        5.2.2   Break-Up of Fluid Droplets 102
    5.3   Mixing Devices 104
        5.3.1   Banbury Mixer...105
        5.3.2   Mixing in Single Screw Extruders.........................106
        5.3.3   Static Mixers..109
        5.3.4   Cokneader..110
        5.3.5   Twin Screw Extruders 111
    Examples..112
    Problems..114

References..115

6 Injection Molding..117

    6.1   The Injection Molding Cycle...118

    6.2   The Injection Molding Machine 126

            6.2.1   The Plasticating and Injection Unit.....................................126

            6.2.2   The Clamping Unit 127

            6.2.3   The Mold Cavity..128

    6.3   Related Injection Molding Processes 131

    6.4   Computer Simulation in Injection Molding...132

    Examples...133

    Problems...137

    References..139

7 Secondary Shaping..141

    7.1   Fiber Spinning 141

    7.2   Film Production..143

            7.2.1   Cast Film Extrusion 143

            7.2.2   Film Blowing...145

    7.3   Blow Molding 148

            7.3.1   Extrusion Blow Molding 149

            7.3.2   Injection Blow Molding...151

    Examples...155

    Problems...157

    References..157

8 Other Important Polymer Processes...159

    8.1   Calendering...159

    8.2   Coating..163

    8.3   Processing Reactive Polymers 167

    8.4   Compression Molding..171

    8.5   Foaming...175

    8.6   Rotational Molding 176

    Examples...177

    Problems...177

    References..178

Appendix 181

A1 Extrusion Laboratory 183

    A1.1 Objective 183

    A1.2 Laboratory Equipment 183

        A1.2.1 Extruder 183

        A1.2.2 Material 184

        A1.2.3 Utilities 184

    A1.3 Experimental Procedure 185

A2 Injection Molding Laboratory 187

    A2.1 Objective 187

    A2.2 Laboratory Equipment 188

        A2.2.1 Injection Molder 188

        A2.2.2 Utilities 189

    A2.3 Experimental Procedure 189

A3 Blow Molding Laboratory 195

    A3.1 Objective 195

    A3.2 Laboratory Equipment 195

        A3.2.1 Blow Molder 195

        A3.2.2 Utilities 195

    A3.3 Experimental Procedure 196

A4 Thermoforming Laboratory 201

    A4.1 Objective 201

    A4.2 Laboratory Equipment 201

        A4.2.1 Thermoforming Machine 201

        A4.2.2 Utilities 203

    A4.3 Experimental Procedure 203

A5 Film Blowing Laboratory 207

    A5.1 Objective 207

    A5.2 Laboratory Equipment 207

        A5.2.2 Utilities 207

    A5.3 Experimental Procedure 209

A6   Transport Phenomena Equations...213

A7   Properties Table...217

Subject Index...227

Biography...231

1 Introduction to Polymers

As the word suggests, polymers* are materials composed of molecules of high molecular weight. These large molecules are generally called *macromolecules*. The unique material properties of polymers and versatility of processing methods are attributed to their molecular structure. The ease with which polymers and *plastics* ** are processed makes them, for many applications, the most sought after materials today. Because of their low density and their ability to be shaped and molded at relatively low temperatures, compared to traditional materials such as metals, plastics and polymers are the material of choice when integrating several parts into a single component—a design step usually called *part consolidation*. In fact, parts and components, traditionally made of wood, metal, ceramics, or glass, are frequently redesigned with plastics.

1.1 Historical Background

Natural polymeric materials such as rubber have been in use for thousands of years. Natural rubber also known as *caoutchouc* (crying trees) has been used by South American Indians in the manufacture of waterproof containers, shoes, torches, and squeeze bulb pumps. The first Spanish explorers of Haiti and Mexico reported that natives played games on clay courts with rubber balls [1]. Rubber trees were first mentioned in *De Orbe Novo*, originally published in Latin, by Pietro Martire d'Anghiera in 1516. The French explorer and mathematician Charles Maria de la Condamine, who was sent to Peru by the French *Academie des Sciences*, brought caoutchouc from South America to Europe in the 1740s. In his report [2] he mentions several rubber items made by native South Americans including a pistonless pump composed of a rubber pear with a hole in the bottom. He points out that the most remarkable property of natural rubber is its great elasticity.

The first chemical investigations on *gummi elasticum* were published by the Frenchman Macquer in 1761. However, it was not until the 20th century that the molecular architecture of polymers was well understood. Soon after its introduction to Europe, various uses were found for natural rubber. Gossart manufactured the first polymer tubes in 1768 by wrapping rubber sheets around glass pipes. During the same time period small rubber blocks where introduced to erase lead pencil marks from paper. In fact, the word *rubber* originates from this specific application—*rubbing*.

These new materials slowly evolved from novelty status as a result of new applications and processing equipment. Although the screw press, the predecessor of today's compression molding press, was patented in 1818 by McPherson Smith [3], the first documented *polymer processing* machinery dates to 1820 when Thomas Hancock invented a rubber masticator. This masticator, consisting of a toothed rotor in a toothed cylindrical

---

* From the Greek, *poli* which means many, and *meros* which means parts.
** The term plastics describes the compound of a polymer with one or more additives.

cavity [4], was used to reclaim rubber scraps which resulted from the manual manufacturing process of elastic straps, perhaps the first recycling effort. In 1833 the development of the vulcanization process by Charles Goodyear [5] greatly enhanced the properties of natural rubber, and in 1836 Edwin M. Chaffee invented the two roll steam heated mill, the predecessor of the calender, for continuously mixing additives into rubber for the manufacture of rubber-coated textiles and leathers. As early as 1845, presses and dies were used to mold buttons, jewelry, dominoes, and other novelties out of shellac and gutta-percha. *Gutta-percha* (rubber clump), a gum found in trees similar to rubber, became the first wire insulation and was used for ocean cable insulation for many years.

The ram-type extruder was invented by Henry Bewley and Richard Brooman in 1845. The first *polymer processing* screw extruder, the most influential equipment in polymer processing, was patented by an Englishman named Mathew Gray in 1879 for the purpose of wire coating. However, the screw pump is attributed to Archimedes, and the actual invention of the screw extruder by A.G. DeWolfe of the U.S. dates back to the early 1860s.

Cellulose nitrate plasticized by camphor, possibly the first thermoplastic, was patented by Isaiah and John Hyatt in 1870. Based on experience from metal injection molding, the Hyatt brothers built and patented the first injection molding machine in 1872 to mold cellulose materials [6].

With the mass production of rubber, gutta-percha, cellulose, and shellac articles during the height of the industrial revolution, the polymer processing industry after 1870 saw the invention and development of internal kneading and mixing machines for the processing and preparation of raw materials [7]. A notable invention was the Banbury mixer, developed by Fernley Banbury in 1916. This mixer, with some modifications, is still used for rubber compounding.

Bakelite, developed by Leo Baekeland in 1907, was the first synthetically developed polymer. Bakelite, also known as phenolic, is a thermoset resin that reacts by condensation polymerization occurring when phenol and formaldehyde are mixed and heated.

In 1924, Hermann Staudinger proposed a model that described polymers as linear molecular chains. Once this model was accepted by other scientists, the concept used to synthesize new materials was realized. In 1927 cellulose acetate and polyvinyl chloride (PVC) [8] were developed. Because of its higher wear resistance, polyvinyl chloride replaced shellac for phonograph records in the early 1930s. Wallace Carothers pioneered condensation polymers such as polyesters and polyamides. It was not until this point that the scientific world was finally convinced of the validity of Staudinger's work. Polyamides, first called Nylon, were set into production in 1938. Polyvinyl acetate, acrylic polymers, polystyrene (PS), polyurethanes, and melamine were also developed in the 1930s [9].

The first single screw extruder designed for the processing of thermoplastic polymers was built circa 1935 at the Paul Troester Maschinenfabrik [10]. Around that same time period, Roberto Colombo developed a twin screw extruder for thermoplastics.

World War II and the post-war years saw accelerated development of new polymeric materials. Polyethylene (PE), polytetrafluoroethylene, epoxies, and acrylonitrile-butadiene-styrene (ABS) were developed in the 1940s, and linear polyethylene, polypropylene (PP), polyacetal, polyethylene terephthalate (PET), polycarbonate (PC), and many more materials came in the 1950s. The 1970s saw the development of new polymers such as polyphenylene sulfide and the 1980s, liquid crystalline polymers.

Developing and synthesizing new polymeric materials has become increasingly expensive and difficult. Developing new engineering materials by blending or mixing two or more polymers or by modifying existing ones with plasticizers is now widely accepted.

The world's yearly production of polymer resins has experienced steady growth since the turn of the century, with growth predicted well into the 21st century. Figure 1.1 [11] presents the world's yearly polymer production in millions of tons. In developed countries, the growth in annual polymer production has decreased recently. However, developing countries in South America and Asia are now starting to experience tremendous growth.

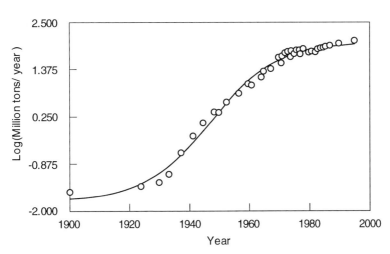

Figure 1.1   World yearly plastics production since 1900

Of the more than 31 million tons of polymers produced in the U.S. in 1993, 90% were thermoplastics. Figure 1.2 breaks the U.S. polymer production into major polymer categories, including polyethylenes, polypropylene, polystyrene, polyvinyl chloride, and thermosets. Polyethylenes are by far the most widely used polymeric material, accounting for 41% of the U.S. plastic production.

1.2 General Properties

Any plastic resin can be categorized as either a thermoplastic or thermoset. Thermoplastics are those polymers that solidify as they cool, restricting the motion of the long molecules. When heated, these materials regain the ability to "flow," as the molecules can slide past each other easily. Thermoplastic polymers further are divided into two classes: amorphous and semi-crystalline polymers.

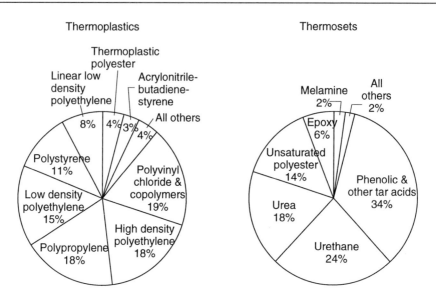

Figure 1.2   Break down of U.S. polymer production into major polymer categories
Source: SPI Committee on Resin Statistics as compiled by Ernst & Young

Amorphous thermoplastics have molecules that remain disorderly as they cool, leading to a material with a random molecular structure. An amorphous polymer solidifies, or vitrifies, as it cools below its glass transition temperature, T_g. Semi-crystalline thermoplastics, on the other hand, solidify with a certain order in their molecular structure. Hence, as they cool, they harden when the molecules arrange in a regular order below what is usually called the melting temperature, T_m. The molecules in semi-crystalline polymers not ordered remain in amorphous regions. These regions within the semi-crystalline domains solidify at the glass transition temperature. Most semi-crystalline polymers have a glass transition temperature below the ice point, and, behave at room temperature similarly to rubbery or leathery materials. Table 1.1 presents the most common amorphous and semi-crystalline thermoplastics with some of their applications.

On the other hand, thermosetting polymers solidify by a chemical cure. Here, the long macromolecules crosslink during cure, resulting in a network. The original molecules can no longer slide past each other. These networks prevent "flow" even after re-heating. The high density of crosslinking between the molecules makes thermosetting materials stiff and brittle. Thermosets also exhibit glass transition temperatures which sometimes exceed thermal degradation temperatures. Some of the most common thermosets and their applications are also found in Table 1.1.

Compared to thermosets, elastomers are only slightly crosslinked, which permits almost full moleculer extension. However, the links across the molecules hinder them from sliding past each other, making even large deformations reversible. One common characteristic of elastomeric materials is that the glass transition temperature is much lower than room temperature. Table 1.1 lists the most common elastomers with some of their applications.

Table 1.1 Common Polymers and Some of Their Applications

Polymer	Some Applications
	Thermoplastics
Amorphous	
Polystyrene	Mass-produced transparent articles, packaging, insulation (foamed)
Polymethyl methacrylate	Skylights, airplane windows, lenses, stop lights
Polycarbonate	Helmets, hockey masks, blinker lights, head lights
Unplasticized polyvinyl chloride	Tubes, window frames, siding, bottles, packaging
Plasticized polyvinyl chloride	Shoes, hoses, calendered films and sheets (floors and upholstery)
Semi-crystalline	
High density polyethylene	Milk and soap bottles, mass produced household goods
Low density polyethylene	Mass produced household goods, grocery bags
Polypropylene	Housings for electric appliances, auto battery cases
Polytetrafluoroethylene	Coating of cooking pans, lubricant-free bearings
Polyamide	Gears, bolts, skate wheels, pipes, fishing line, textiles, ropes
	Thermosets
Epoxy	Adhesive, matrix in fiber-reinforced composite parts
Melamine	Decorative heat-resistant surfaces for kitchens and furniture, dishes
Phenolics	Heat-resistant handles for pans, irons and toasters, electric outlets
Unsaturated polyester	Sinks and tubs, automotive body panels (with glass fiber)
	Elastomers
Polybutadiene	Automotive tires, golf ball skin
Ethylene propylene rubber	Automotive radiator hoses and window seals, roof covering
Natural rubber (polyisoprene)	Automotive tires, engine mounts
Polyurethane elastomer	Roller skate wheels, automotive seats (foamed), shoe soles (foamed)
Silicone rubber	Seals, flexible hoses for medical applications
Styrene butadiene rubber	Automotive tire treads

As mentioned earlier, there are thousands of grades of polymers available to the design engineer. These cover a wide range of properties, from soft to hard, ductile to brittle, and weak to tough. Figure 1.3 shows this range by plotting important average properties for selected polymers. The abbreviations used in Fig. 1.3 are defined in Table 1.2. The values for each material in Fig. 1.3 are representative averages.

The relatively low stiffness of polymeric materials is attributed to their molecular structure, which allows relative movement with ease while under stress. However, the strength and stiffness of individual polymer chains are much higher than the measured properties of the bulk. For example, polyethylene whose molecules have a theoretical stiffness of 300,000 MPa, has a bulk stiffness of only 1,000 MPa [12,13]. By introducing high molecular orientation, the stiffness and strength of a polymer can be substantially increased. In the case of *ultra-drawn, ultra high molecular weight high density polyethylene,* UHMHDPE, fibers can exceed a stiffness 200,000 MPa [13].

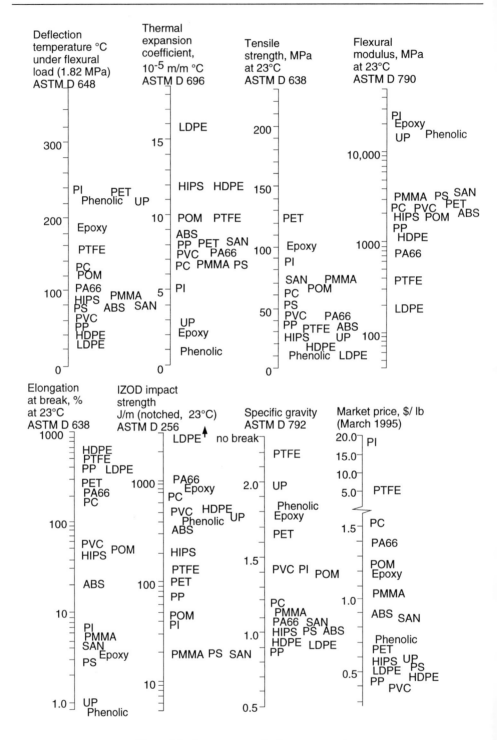

Figure 1.3 Average properties for common polymers

Table 1.2 Abbreviation of Common Polymers

Polymer	ASTM D1600-93 abbreviation
Acrylonitrile-butadiene-styrene	ABS
Epoxy	EP
High density polyethylene	HDPE
Impact resistant polystyrene	IPS (HIPS)
Low density polyethylene	LDPE
Phenol-formaldehyde (Phenolic)	PF
Polyacetal (polyoxymethylene)	POM
Polyamide 66	PA 66
Polycarbonate	PC
Polyethylene terephthalate	PET
Polyimide	PI
Polymethyl methacrylate	PMMA
Polypropylene	PP
Polystyrene	PS
Polytetrafluoroethylene	PTFE
Polyvinyl chloride	PVC
Styrene-acrylonitrile copolymer	SAN
Unsaturated polyester	UP

1.3 Macromolecular Structure of Polymers

Polymers are macromolecular structures generated synthetically or through natural processes. Cotton, silk, natural rubber, ivory, amber and wood are a few materials that occur naturally with an organic macromolecular structure, whereas natural inorganic materials include quartz and glass. The other class of organic materials with a macromolecular structure are synthetic polymers, which are generated through addition polymerization or condensation polymerization.

In addition polymerization, monomers are added to each other by breaking the double-bonds that exist between carbon atoms, allowing them to link to neighboring carbon atoms to form long chains. The simplest example is the addition of ethylene monomers, schematically shown in Fig. 1.4, to form polyethylene molecules as shown in Fig. 1.5. The schematic shown in Fig. 1.5 can also be written symbolically as shown in Fig. 1.6. Here, the subscript n represents the number of repeat units which determines the molecular weight of a polymer. The number of repeat units is more commonly referred to as the degree of polymerization.

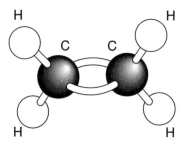

Figure 1.4   Schematic representation of an ethylene monomer

Another technique for producing macromolecular materials is condensation polymerization. Condensation polymerization occurs when two components with end-groups that react with each other are mixed. When they are stoichiometric, these end-groups react, linking them to chains and leaving a by-product such as water. A common polymer made by condensation polymerization is polyamide where diamine and diacid groups react to form polyamide and water as shown in Fig. 1.7.

In the molecular level, there are several forces that hold a polymeric material together. The most basic forces are the covalent bonds which hold the polymer backbone together, such as the -C-C- or -C-N- bond.

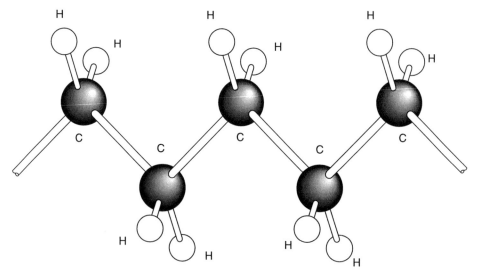

Figure 1.5   A polyethylene molecule

Figure 1.6   Symbolic representation of a polyethylene molecule

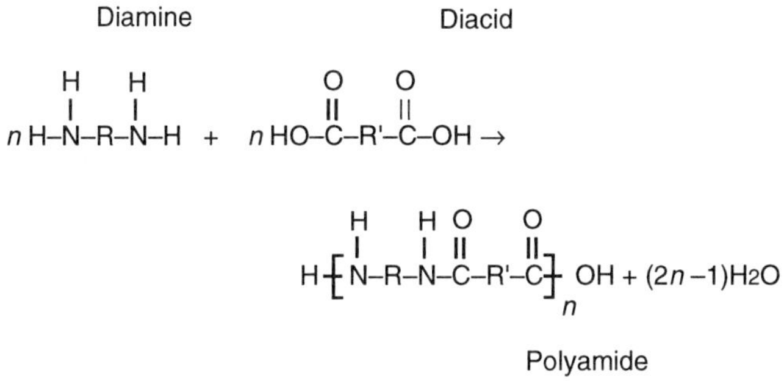

Diamine   Diacid

$$n\ \overset{\overset{\displaystyle H}{\displaystyle |}}{H}-N-R-\overset{\overset{\displaystyle H}{\displaystyle |}}{N}-H\ +\ n\ HO-\overset{\overset{\displaystyle O}{\displaystyle ||}}{C}-R'-\overset{\overset{\displaystyle O}{\displaystyle ||}}{C}-OH\ \rightarrow$$

$$H\left[\overset{\overset{\displaystyle H}{\displaystyle |}}{N}-R-\overset{\overset{\displaystyle H}{\displaystyle |}}{N}-\overset{\overset{\displaystyle O}{\displaystyle ||}}{C}-R'-\overset{\overset{\displaystyle O}{\displaystyle ||}}{C}\right]_n OH\ +\ (2n-1)H_2O$$

Polyamide

Figure 1.7   Symbolic representation of the condensation polymerization of polyamide

1.4 Molecular Weight

A polymeric material usually consists of polymer chains of various lengths. With the exception of some naturally occurring polymers, most polymers have a molecular weight distribution such as shown in Fig. 1.8 and the molecular weight is described by a set of averages. The properties of polymeric material are strongly linked to the molecular weight of the polymer as shown schematically in Fig. 1.9. A polymer such as polystyrene is stiff and brittle at room temperature with a degree of polymerization of 1,000. However, at a degree of polymerization of 10, polystyrene is sticky and soft at room temperature. The stiffness properties reach an asymptotic maximum, whereas the flow temperature increases with molecular weight. One must find the molecular weight of a polymer that renders ideal mechanical properties, while maintaining flow properties that make it easy to shape the material during manufacturing.

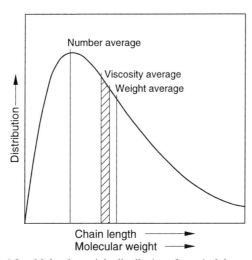

Figure 1.8   Molecular weight distribution of a typical thermoplastic

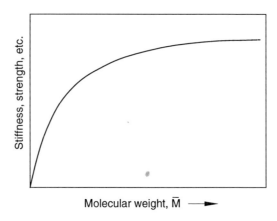

Figure 1.9   Influence of molecular weight on mechanical properties

Polymer chain Branching, which occurs due to irregularities during polymerization, also influences the final structure, crystallinity and properties of the polymeric material. Figure 1.10 shows the molecular architecture of high density, low density and linear low density polyethylenes (LLDPE). The high density polyethylene (HDPE) has between 5 and 10 short branches every 1000 carbon atoms. The low density material (LDPE) has the same number of branches as HDPE; however, they are much longer and are themselves usually branched. The LLDPE has between 10 and 35 short chains every 1000 carbon atoms. Polymer chains with fewer and shorter branches can crystallize more easily resulting in higher density.

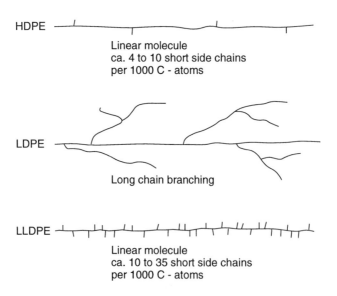

Figure 1.10   Schematic of the molecular structure of different polyethylenes

1.5 Arrangement of Polymer Molecules

Polymeric materials can be categorized as either thermoplastics or thermosets. Thermoplastics can remelt after solidification, and thermosets solidify via a chemical reaction that causes polymer molecules to crosslink. These crosslinked materials cannot be remelted after solidification.

As thermoplastic polymers solidify, they take on two different types of structure: amorphous and semi-crystalline. Amorphous polymers are those where the molecules solidify in a random arrangement, whereas the molecules in semi-crystalline polymers align with their neighbors, forming regions with a three-dimensional order.

1.5.1 Thermoplastic Polymers

The formation of macromolecules from monomers occurs if there are unsaturated carbon atoms (carbon atoms connected with double or triple bonds), or if there are monomers with reactive end-groups. For example, in an ethylene monomer a double bond is split which frees two valence electrons per monomer and leads to the formation of a macromolecule such as polyethylene. This process is called polymerization. Similarly, two complementing monomers (R and R') that each posess two reactive end groups (bifunctional) can react with each other, also leading to the formation of a polymer chain.

1.5.2 Amorphous Thermoplastics

Amorphous thermoplastics, with their randomly arranged molecular structure, are analogous to spaghetti. Because of their structure, the characteristic size of the largest ordered region is length of a carbon-carbon bond. This dimension is much smaller than the wavelength of visible light and so generally makes amorphous thermoplastics very clear, and in most cases close to transparent.

Figure 1.11 [14] shows the shear modulus, G', versus temperature for polystyrene, one of the most common amorphous thermoplastics. The figure, which was obtained through a dynamic-mechanical test, shows two general regions: one where the modulus appears fairly constant, and one where the modulus drops significantly with increasing temperature. With decreasing temperatures, the material enters the glassy region where the slope of the modulus approaches zero. At high temperatures, the modulus is negligible and the material is soft enough to flow. Although there is no clear transition between "solid" and "liquid," the temperature dividing the two states in an amorphous thermoplastic is called the *glass transition temperature* T_g. For the polystyrene in Fig. 1.11, the glass transition temperature is about 110 °C. Although data is usually presented in the form shown in Fig. 1.11, the curve shown in the figure was measured at a constant frequency. If the test frequency is increased—reducing the time scale—the curve shifts to the right, because higher temperatures are required to achieve molecular motion at the new frequency.

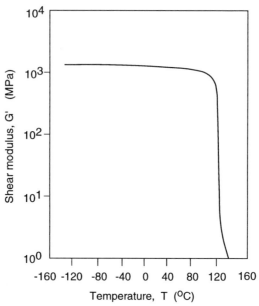

Figure 1.11   Shear modulus of polystyrene as a function of temperature

1.5.3 Semi-Crystalline Thermoplastics

The molecules in semi-crystalline thermoplastic polymers align in an ordered crystal structure as shown for polyethylene in Fig. 1.12. The schematic shows the general structure and hierarchical arrangement in semi-crystalline materials. The crystalline structure is part of a *lamellar crystal* which in turn forms the *spherulites.* The sperulitic structure is the largest domain with a specific order and has a characteristic size of 50 to 500 μm. This is much larger than the wavelength of visible light, making semi-crystalline materials translucent, not transparent.

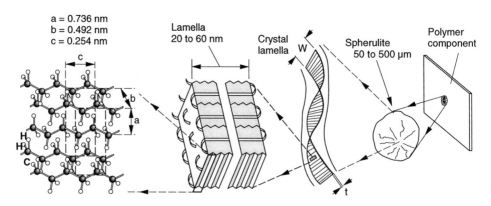

Figure 1.12   Schematic representation of the general molecular structure and arrangement of typical semi-crystalline materials

However, the crystalline regions are tiny with molecular chains comprised of both crystalline and amorphous regions. The degree of crystallinity in a typical thermoplastic varies from grade to grade. For example, in polyethylene, the degree of crystallinity depends on the branching and the cooling rate. LDPE with its long branches (Fig.1.10) can only crystallize to about 40 to 50%, whereas a HDPE crystallizes to up to 80%. The density and strength of semi-crystalline thermoplastics increase with the degree of crystallinity.

Figure 1.13 [14] shows the dynamic shear modulus versus temperature for a HDPE, the most common semi-crystalline thermoplastic. Again, this curve presents data measured at one test frequency. The figure clearly shows two distinct transitions: one at about -110 °C, the *glass transition temperature* and another near 140 °C, the *melting temperature*. Above the melting temperature, the shear modulus is negligible and the material flows. Crystalline arrangement begins to develop as the temperature dips below the melting point. Between the melting and glass transition temperatures, the material behavior is leathery. As the temperature dips below the glass transition temperature, the amorphous regions within the semi-crystalline structure solidify, forming a glassy, stiff, and sometimes brittle polymer.

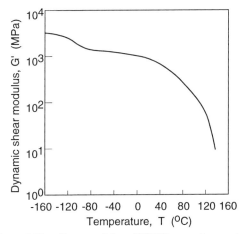

Figure 1.13   Shear modulus of HDPE versus temperature

1.5.4 Thermosets and Crosslinked Elastomers

Thermosets and some elastomers are polymeric materials that can crosslink. The cross-linking causes the material to resist heat after solidification. A more in-depth explanation of the crosslinking chemical reaction that occurs during solidification is given in section 8.3.

Crosslinking is usually a result of double bonds breaking, allowing molecules to link with their neighbors. One of the oldest thermosetting polymers is phenol-formaldehyde or phenolic. Figure 1.14 shows the chemical symbol representation of the reaction. The phenol and formaldehyde molecules react to create a three-dimensional cross-linked network that is stiff and strong. The by-product of this chemical reaction is water.

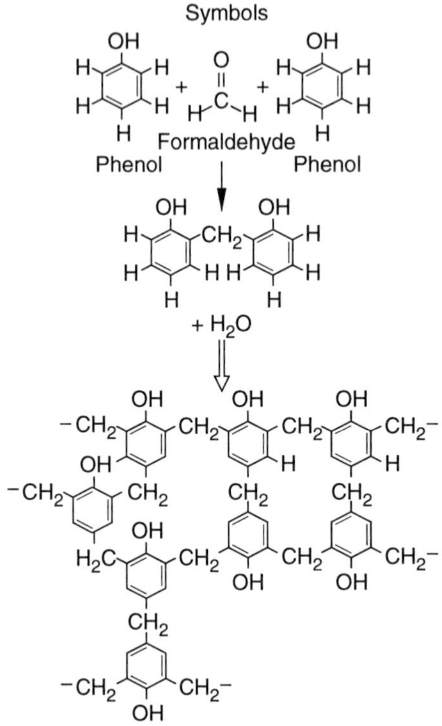

Figure 1.14 Symbolic representation of the condensation polymerization of phenol-formaldehyde resins

1.6 Copolymers and Polymer Blends

Copolymers are polymeric chains of materials with two or more monomer types. A copolymer that is composed of two monomer types is called a *bipolymer*, and one formed from three different monomer groups is called a *terpolymer*. Depending on how the different monomers are arranged in the polymer chain, distinguishes them as *random, alternating, block,* or *graft* copolymers. These copolymer types are schematically represented in Fig. 1.15.

A widely used copolymer is high impact polystyrene (PS-HI), formed by grafting polystyrene to polybutadiene. If styrene and butadiene are randomly copolymerized, the resulting material is an elastomer called styrene-butadiene-rubber (SBR). Another classic example of copolymerization is the terpolymer acrylonitrile-butadiene-styrene (ABS).

Polymer blends belong to another family of polymeric materials which are made by mixing or blending two or more polymers to enhance the physical properties of each individual component. Common polymer blends include PP+PC, PVC+ABS, PE+PTFE, and ABS+PC.

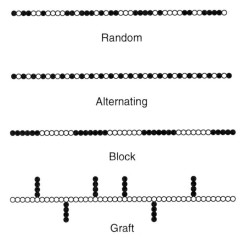

Figure1.15   Schematic representation of different copolymers

1.7 Polymer Additives

A polymer seldom is sold as a pure material. More often a polymer contains several additives to aid during processing, add color, or enhance the mechanical properties.

1.7.1 Plasticizers

Solvents, commonly called plasticizers, are sometimes mixed into a polymer to dramatically alter its rheological or mechanical properties. Plasticizers are used as processing aids since they have the same effect as raising the temperature of the material. The resulting lowered viscosities reduce the risk of thermal degradation during processing. For example, cellulose nitrite thermally degrades if it is processed without a plasticizer.

Plasticizers are more commonly used to alter a polymer's mechanical properties such as stiffness, toughness, and strength. For example, adding a plasticizer such as dioctylphthalate (DOP) to PVC can reduce its stiffness by three orders of magnitude and can lower its glass transition temperature by 35 °C. In fact, highly plasticized PVC is rubbery at room temperature.

1.7.2 Flame Retardants

Since polymers are organic materials, most of them are flammable. The flammability of polymers has always been a serious technical problem. However, some additives that contain halogens, such as bromine or chlorine or phosphorous, reduce the possibility of either ignition within a polymer component or once ignited, flame spread. Bromine is more effective flame retardant than chlorine.

1.7.3 Stabilizers

The combination of heat and oxygen can result in thermal degradation in a polymer. Heat or energy produce free radicals which react with oxygen to form carbonyl compounds, giving rise to yellow or brown discolorations in the final product.

Thermal degradation can be suppressed by adding stabilizers, such as antioxidants or peroxide decomposers. These additives do not eliminate thermal degradation but slow it down. Once the stabilizer has been consumed by reaction with oxygen, the polymer is no longer protected against thermal degradation.

Polyvinyl chloride is probably the polymer most vulnerable to thermal degradation. In polyvinyl chloride, scission of the C-Cl bond occurs in the weakest point of the molecule. The chlorine radicals react with their nearest CH group, forming HCl and creating new weak C-Cl bonds. A stabilizer must therefore be used to neutralize HCl and stop the autocatalytic reaction, as well as preventing corrosion of processing equipment.

1.7.4 Antistatic Agents

Since polymers have such low electrical conductivity, they can easily build-up electric charges. The amount of charge build-up is controlled by the rate at which the charge is generated compared to the charge decay. The rate of charge generation at the surface of the component can be reduced by reducing the intimacy of contact, whereas the rate of charge decay is increased through surface conductivity. Hence, a good antistatic agent should be an ionizable additive that allows the charge to migrate to the surface. At the same time it should be creating bridges to the atmosphere through moisture in the surroundings. Typical antistatic agents are nitrogen compounds, such as long chain amines, and amides and polyhydric alcohols.

1.7.5 Fillers

Fillers can be classified three ways: those that reinforce the polymer and improve its mechanical performance; those used to take-up space and so reduce the amount of resin to produce a part – sometimes referred to as *extenders*; and those, less common, that are dispersed through the polymer to improve its electric conductivity.

Polymers that contain fillers that improve its mechanical performance are often referred to as reinforced plastics or *composites*. Composites can be furthermore divided into composites with *high performance* reinforcements, and composites with *low performance* reinforcements. The high performance composites are those where the reinforcement is placed inside the polymer so that optimal mechanical behavior is achieved, such as unidirectional glass fibers in an epoxy resin. High performance composites usually have 50 to 80% reinforcement by volume and usually have a laminated tubular shape containing braided reinforcements. The low performance composites are those where the reinforcement is small enough that it can be well dispersed into the matrix. These materials can be processed the same way as their unreinforced counterparts.

The most common filler used to reinforce polymeric materials is glass fiber. However, wood fiber, which is commonly used as an extender, also increases the stiffness and mechanical performance of some thermoplastics. To improve the bonding between the polymer matrix and the reinforcement, *coupling agents* such as *silanes* and *titanates* are often added.

Extenders, used to reduce the cost of the component, are often particulate fillers. The most common of these are calcium carbonate, silica flour, clay, and wood flour or fiber. As mentioned earlier, some fillers also slightly reinforce the polymer matrix, such as clay, silica flour, and wood fiber. Polymers with extenders often have significantly lower toughness than when unfilled.

1.7.6 Blowing Agents

The task of blowing or foaming agents is to produce cellular polymers, also called expanded plastics. The cells can be completely enclosed (closed cell) or can be interconnected (open cell). Polymer foams are produced with densities between 1.6 kg/m^3 and 960 kg/m^3. There are many reasons for using polymer foams, such as their high strength to weight ratio, excellent insulating and acoustic properties, and high energy and vibration absorbing properties.

Polymer foams can be made by mechanically whipping gases into the polymer, or by either chemical or physical means. The basic steps of the foaming process are (1) cell nucleation, (2) expansion or growth of the cells and (3) stabilization of the cells. Cell nucleation occurs when, at a given temperature and pressure, the solubility of a gas is reduced, leading to saturation, and expelling the excess gas to form bubbles. Nucleating agents are used for initial formation of a bubble. The bubble reaches an equilibrium shape when the pressure in the bubble balances the surface tension.

Examples

1.1   Estimate the degree of polymerization of a polypropylene with an average molecular weight of 100,000.

As shown in the diagram below the repeat unit of a polypropylene molecule contains 3 carbon and 6 hydrogen atoms.

$$\left[\begin{array}{cc} H & H \\ | & | \\ C & - C \\ | & | \\ H & CH_3 \end{array}\right]_n$$

From the diagram we can see that each repeat unit's molecular weight is $6(1) + 3(12) = 42$. Thus, a molecule with a molecular weight of 100,000 is formed by $100,000/42 = 2381$ repeat units.

Problems

1.1 Estimate the degrees of polymerization of a polyethylene with an average molecular weight between 150,000 and 200,000.

1.2 What is the maximum possible separation between the ends of a polystyrene molecule with a molecular weight of 160,000 ?

1.3 Write the molecular structure for the following polymers: polyacetal, polycarbonate, polyvinyl chloride, polystyrene, and polytetrafluoroethylene.

References

1. Stern, H.J., *Rubber: Natural and Synthetic*, Maclaren and Sons LDT (1967), London
2. de la Condamine, C.M.,*Relation Abregee D'un Voyage Fait Dans l'interieur de l'Amerique Meridionale*, Academie des Sciences (1745), Paris
3. DuBois, J.H., *Plastics History U.S.A.*, Cahners Publishing Co., Inc. (1972), Boston
4. Tadmor, Z., and C.G. Gogos, *Principles of Polymer Processing*, John Wiley & Sons
5. McPherson, A.T., and A. Klemin, *Engineering Uses of Rubber*, Reinhold Publishing Corporation (1956), New York
6. Sonntag, R., *Kunststoffe* (1985), *75*, 4
7. Herrmann, H., *Kunststoffe* (1985), *75*, 2
8. Regnault, H.V. Liebigs Ann. (1835), 14, 22
9. Ulrich, H., *Introduction to Industrial Polymers*, 2nd Ed., Hanser Publishers (1993), Munich
10. Rauwendaal, C., *Polymer Extrusion*, 2nd Ed., Hanser publishers (1990), Munich
11. Utracki, L.A., *Polym. Eng. Sci.* (1995), 35, 1, 2
12. Termonia, Y., and P. Smith, *High Modulus Polymers*, A.E. Zachariades, and R.S. Porter, Eds., Marcel Dekker Inc. (1988), New York
13. Ehrenstein, G.W., Faserverbundkunststoffe, Carl Hanser Verlag (1992), München
14. Domininghaus, H., *Plastics for Engineers*, Hanser Publishers (1993), Munich

2 Mechanical Behavior of Polymers

The mechanical properties of a polymeric component are dominated by its viscoelasticity. This is reflected by the time-dependency of the mechanical response of a component during loading. Hence, a polymer behaves differently if subjected to short term or long term loads. This chapter briefly explains polymer viscoelasticity and covers the short and long term mechanical behavior of polymers.

2.1 Viscoelastic Behavior of Polymers

A polymer, at a specific temperature and molecular weight, may behave as a liquid or a solid depending on the speed (time scale) at which its molecules deform. This behavior, which ranges between liquid and solid, is generally referred to as the viscoelastic behavior or material response. This discussion is limited to *linear viscoelasticity*, which is valid for polymer systems undergoing *small* or *slow deformations*. *Non-linear viscoelasticity* is required when modeling *large rapid deformations,* such as those encountered in flowing polymer melts.

In linear viscoelasticity, the *stress relaxation test* is often used, along with the *time-temperature superposition principle* and the *Boltzmann superposition principle*, to explain the behavior of polymeric materials during deformation.

2.1.1 Stress Relaxation

In a stress relaxation test, a polymer specimen is suddenly deformed a fixed amount, ε_0, and the stress required to hold that amount of deformation is recorded over time. This test is cumbersome to perform, so the design engineer and the material scientist have tended to ignore it. In fact, the standard relaxation test, ASTM D2991, was recently dropped by ASTM. Rheologists and scientists, however, have consistently used the stress relaxation test to interpret the viscoelastic behavior of polymers.

Figure 2.1 [1] presents the stress relaxation modulus measured for polyisobutylene[*] at various temperatures. Here, the stress relaxation modulus is defined by

$$E_r(t) = \frac{\sigma(t)}{\varepsilon_0} \tag{2.1}$$

where ε_0 is the applied strain and $\sigma(t)$ the stress being measured. From the test results, stress relaxation is clearly time and temperature dependent, especially around the glass transition temperature where the curve is steepest. For the polyisobutylene in Fig. 2.1, the glass transition temperature is about -70 °C. The measurements were completed in an experimental time window between a few seconds and one day. The tests performed at

---

[*] Better known as the matrix material for chewing gum.

lower temperatures were used to record the initial relaxation while these at higher temperatures only captured the end of relaxation of the rapidly decaying stresses.

The time it takes for the imposed stresses to relax is governed by the relaxation time, λ. High temperatures lead to small molecular relaxation times and low temperatures lead to materials with long relaxation times. When changing temperature, the shape of relaxation test results remains the same, except for a horizontal shift to the left or right, representing lower or higher response times, respectively.

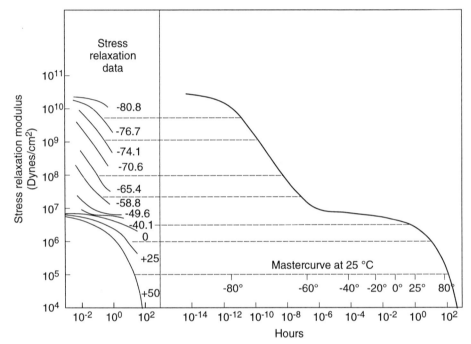

Figure 2.1   Relaxation modulus curves for polyisobutylene and corresponding master curve at 25 °C

2.1.2 Time-Temperature Superposition

The time-temperature equivalence seen in stress relaxation test results can be used to reduce data at various temperatures to one general *master curve* for a reference temperature, T. To generate a master curve at any reference temperature, the curves shown on the left of Fig. 2.1 must be shifted horizontally, holding the reference curve fixed. The master curve for the data in Fig. 2.1 is on the right of the figure. Each curve was shifted horizontally until the ends of all the curves superposed. The amount that each curve was shifted can be plotted with respect to the temperature difference taken from the reference temperature. For the data in Fig. 2.1, the shift factor is shown in Fig. 2.2 .

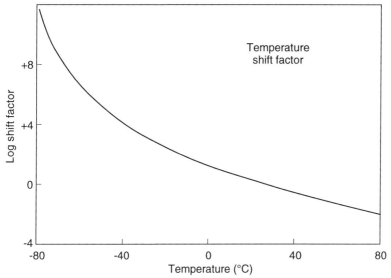

Figure 2.2   Shift factor as a function of temperature used to generate the master curve plotted in Fig. 2.1

WLF EQUATION [2]

The amount relaxation curves must be shifted in the time axis to line-up with the master curve at a reference temperarture is represented by

$$\log t - \log t_{ref} = \log\left(\frac{t}{t_{ref}}\right) = \log a_T \qquad (2.2)$$

Although the results in Figure 2.2 where shifted to a reference temperature of 298 K (25 ^{o}C), Williams, Landel and Ferry [2] chose T_{ref} = 243 K for

$$\log_{10} a_T = \frac{-8.86(T - T_{ref})}{101.6 + T - T_{ref}} \qquad (2.3)$$

which holds for nearly all amorphous polymers if the chosen reference temperature is 45 K above the glass transition temperature. In general, the horizontal shift, $\log a_T$, between the relaxation responses at various temperatures to a reference temperature can be computed using the well known Williams-Landel-Ferry [2] (WLF) equation. The WLF equation is

$$\log_{10} a_T = -\frac{C_1(T - T_{ref})}{C_2 + (T - T_{ref})} \qquad (2.4)$$

where C_1 and C_2 are material dependent constants. It has been shown that with C_1 = 17.44 and C_2 = 51.6, Eq. 2.4 fits well for a wide variety of polymers as long as the glass transition temperature is chosen as the reference temperature. These values for C_1 and C_2 are often referred to as universal constants. Often, the WLF equation must be adjusted until it fits the experimental data. Master curves of stress relaxation tests are important since the polymer's behavior can be traced over much greater periods than those that can be determined experimentally.

BOLTZMANN SUPERPOSITION PRINCIPLE

In addition to the *time-temperature superposition principle* (WLF), the *Boltzmann suprposition principle* is of extreme importance in the theory of linear viscoelasticity. The Boltzmann superposition principle states that the deformation of a polymer component is the sum or superposition of all strains that result from various loads acting on the part at different times. This means that the response of a material to a specific load is independent of pre-existing loads. Hence, we can compute the deformation of a polymer specimen upon which several loads act at different points in time by simply adding all strain responses.

2.2 The Short-Term Tensile Test

The most commonly used mechanical test is the short-term stress-strain tensile test. Stress-strain curves for selected polymers are displayed in Fig. 2.3 [3]. For comparison, the figure also presents stress-strain curves for copper and steel. Although they have much lower tensile strengths, many engineering polymers exhibit much higher strains at break than metals.

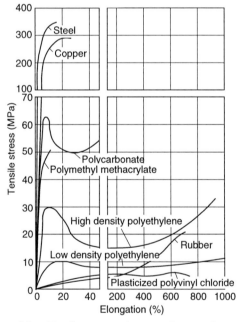

Figure 2.3   Tensile stress-strain curves for several materials

The next two sections discuss the short-term tensile test for cross-linked elastomers and thermoplastic polymers separately. The main reason for separating these two polymers is that the deformation of a crosslinked elastomer and an uncrosslinked thermoplastic differ greatly. The deformation in a crosslinked polymer is generally reversible, while the deformation in typical uncross-linked polymers is associated with molecular chain relaxation, making the process time dependent, and irreversible.

2.2.1 Elastomers

The main feature of cross-linked elastomeric materials is that they can undergo large, reversible deformations. This is because the curled polymer chains stretch during deformation but are hindered from sliding past each other by the crosslinks between the molecules. Once a load is released, most molecules recoil. As an elastomeric polymer component is deformed, the slope in the stress-strain curves drops significantly because the uncurled molecules provide less resistance and entanglement, allowing them to move more freely. Eventually, at deformations of about 400%, the slope starts to increase because the polymer chains are fully stretched. This stretch is followed by polymer chain breakage or crystallization, ending with the fracture of the component. Stress-deformation curves for natural rubber (NR) [4] and a rubber compound [5] composed of 70 parts of styrene-butadiene-rubber (SBR) and 30 parts of natural rubber are shown in Fig. 2.4.

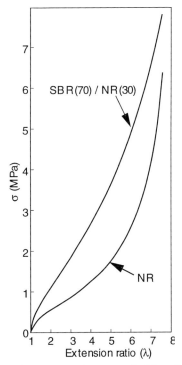

Figure 2.4   Experimental stress-extension curves for NR and a SBR/NR compound

Because of the large deformations, typically several hundred percent, the stress-strain data is usually expressed in terms of the extension ratio, λ, defined by

$$\lambda = \frac{L}{L_0} \tag{2.5}$$

where L and L_0 are the instantaneous and initial lengths of the specimen, respectively.

RUBBER ELASTICITY

For a component in uniaxial extension, or compression, the stress can be computed as

$$\sigma = G_0 \left(\lambda - \frac{1}{\lambda^2} \right) \tag{2.6}$$

where G_0 is the shear modulus at zero extension, which for rubbers can be approximated by

$$G_0 = \frac{E_0}{3} \tag{2.7}$$

with E_0 as the elastic tensile modulus at zero extension. The model agrees with expriments up to about 50% extension ($\lambda = 1.5$). For compression, the model agrees much better with experiments, as shown for natural rubber in Fig. 2.5 [4]. Fortunately, rubber products are rarely deformed more than 25% in compression or tension, allowing the use of the above model.

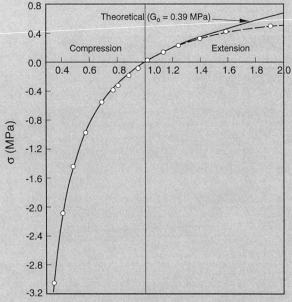

Figure 2.5   Experimental and theoretical stress-extension and compression curves for natural rubber

The corresponding model for equibiaxial extension (inflation) of thin sheets is:

$$\sigma = G_0\left(\lambda^2 - \frac{1}{\lambda^4}\right) \qquad (2.8)$$

2.2.2 Thermoplastic Polymers

Of all the mechanical tests done on thermoplastic polymers, the tensile test is the least understood, and the results are often misinterpreted and misused. Since the test was inherited from other materials that have linear elastic stress-strain responses, it is often inappropriate for testing polymers.

A typical test performed on PMMA at various strain rates at room temperature is shown in Fig. 2.6. The increased curvature in the results with slow elongational speeds suggests that stress relaxation plays a significant role during the test. Here, the high rates of deformation reduce the loading time, allowing higher stress to build-up during the test.

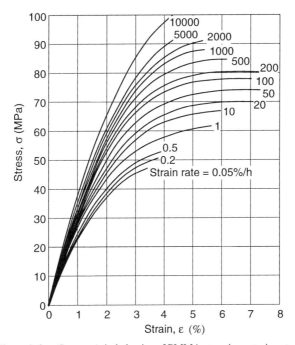

Figure 2.6   Stress-strain behavior of PMMA at various strain rates

MECHANICAL BEHAVIOR OF FILLED POLYMERS

The stiffness and strength of polymers and rubbers is increased by filling them with solid particles such as calcium carbonate and carbon black. The most common expression for describing the effect of carbon black content on the modulus of rubber was originally derived by Guth and Simha [7] for the viscosity of particle suspensions, and later used by Guth [8] to predict the modulus of filled polymers. The Guth equation can be written as

$$\frac{G_f}{G_0} = 1 + 2.5\phi + 14.1\phi^2 \tag{2.9}$$

where G_f is the shear modulus of the filled material and ϕ is the volume fraction of particulate filler. The above expression is compared to experiments [9, 10] in Fig. 2.7.

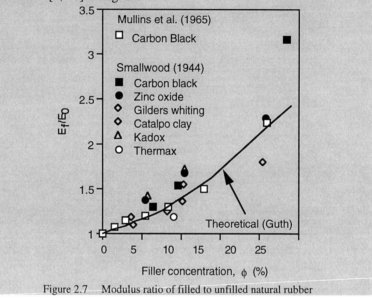

Figure 2.7   Modulus ratio of filled to unfilled natural rubber

2.3 Long-Term Tests

The *stress relaxation* and the *creep* test are well-known long-term tests. The stress relaxation test is difficult to perform and is, therefore, often approximated by data acquired through the more commonly used creep test. The stress relaxation of a polymer is often considered the inverse of creep.

The creep test, which can be performed either in shear, compression, or tension, measures the flow of a polymer component under a constant load. It is a common test that measures the strain, ε, as a function of stress, time, and temperature. Standard creep tests such as DIN 53 444 and ASTM D2990 can be used. Creep tests are performed at a constant temperature, using a range of applied stress, as shown in Fig. 2.8 [11], where the creep responses of a polypropylene copolymer are presented for a range of stresses in a graph with a log scale for time. If plotting creep data in a log-log graph, in the majority of the cases, the creep curves reduce to straight lines. Hence, the creep behavior of most polymers can be approximated with a power law:

$$\varepsilon(t) = M(\sigma, T)t^n \tag{2.10}$$

where M and n are material dependent properties.

As for the stress relaxation test, the creep behavior of a polymer depends heavily on the material temperature during testing, with the highest rates of deformation near the glass transition temperature.

Creep data is often presented in terms of the creep modulus, E_c, defined by

$$E_c = \frac{\sigma_0}{\varepsilon(t)}.$$

(2.11)

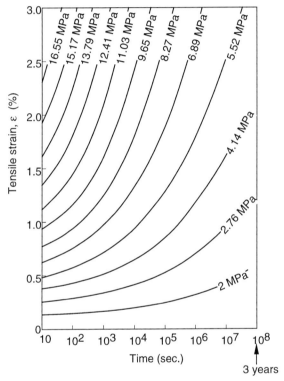

Figure 2.8   Creep response of a propylene-ethylene copolymer at 20 °C

2.3.1 Isochronous and Isometric Creep Plots

Typical creep test data, shown in Fig. 2.8, can be manipulated to be displayed as short-term stress-strain tests or as stress relaxation tests. These manipulated creep curves are called *isochronous* and *isometric* graphs.

An isochronous plot of the creep data is generated by cutting sections through the creep curves at constant times and plotting the stress as a function of strain. The isochronous curves of the creep data in Fig. 2.8 are in Fig. 2.9 [11]. Similar curves can also be generated by performing a series of *short creep tests*, where a specimen is loaded at a specific stress for a short period, typically around 100 seconds [12]. The load is then removed, and the specimen relaxes for a period of at least four times the loading interval. The specimen is then reloaded at a different stress, and the test is repeated until there are sufficient points for an isochronous graph. This procedure is more expedient than the regular creep test and is often used to predict the short-term behavior of polymers. However, it should be pointed out that the short-term tests described in section 2.2.2 are more accurate, quicker, and less expensive to run.

The isometric or "equal size" plots of the creep data are generated by taking constant strain sections of the creep curves and by plotting the stress versus time. Isometric curves of the polypropylene creep data in Fig. 2.8 are in Fig. 2.10 [11]. This plot resembles the stress relaxation test results and is often used similarly. When we divide the stress axis by the strain, we can also plot the modulus versus time.

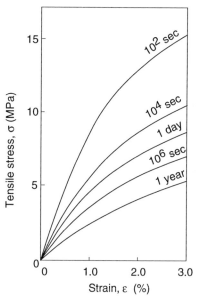

Figure 2.9   Isochronous stress-strain curves for the creep responses in Fig. 2.8

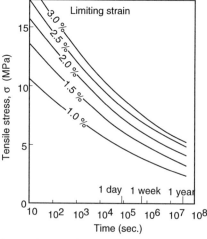

Figure 2.10   Isometric stress-time curves for the creep responses in Fig. 2.8

2.3.2 Creep Rupture

A creeping polymer component eventually undergoes catastrophic failure, generally called creep rupture or static fatigue. The standard test for creep rupture is the same as the creep test discussed earlier. Results from creep rupture tests are usually graphs of applied stress versus the logarithm of time to rupture. An example of a creep rupture test that ran for 10 years is shown in Fig. 2.11 [13,14]. These tests where done between 1958 and 1968 at Hoechst AG, Germany. Here, the creep rupture of HDPE pipes under internal pressures was tested at different temperatures. Two general regions with different slopes become obvious in the plots. The curves to the left of the knee correspond to ductile failure, whereas those to the right correspond to brittle failure. Generating a graph such as the one presented in Fig. 2.11 is lengthy, taking several years of testing. Once the steeper slope, typical of brittle fracture, has been reached, extrapolation with some confidence can be used to estimate future creep rupture times.

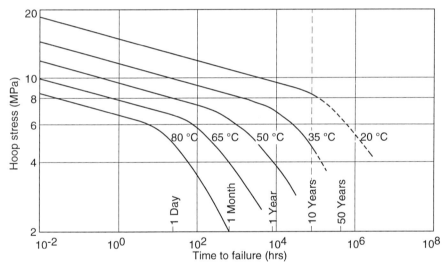

Figure 2.11   Creep rupture behavior as a function of temperature for a HDPE

2.4 Dynamic Mechanical Tests

The sinusoidal oscillatory test, also called the dynamic-mechanical-analysis (DMA) test, is one of the most useful mechanical tests for polymers. Here, a specimen is excited with a low frequency stress input which is recorded along with the strain response. The shapes of the test specimen and the testing procedure vary significantly from test to test. The various tests and their corresponding specimen shapes are described by ASTM D4065 and the terminology is described by ASTM D4092. The typical responses measured in these dynamic tests are a storage modulus, G', and a loss modulus, G". The storage modulus is related to the elastic modulus of the polymer at the loading frequency and the loss modulus to the damping or dissipative component observed during loading. The loss modulus can also be written in terms of loss tangent (tanδ) or logarithmic decrement, Δ. The latter is related to the damping of a freely oscillating specimen.

Figure 2.12 [3] shows the elastic shear modulus and the logarthmic decrement or loss factor for various polypropylene grades. Here, the glass transition temperatures and the melting temperatures can be seen for the various polypropylene grades. The vertical scale in plots such as in Fig. 2.12 is usually logarithmic. However, a linear scale better describes the mechanical behavior of polymers in design aspects. Figure 2.13 [3] presents the elastic shear modulus versus temperature on a linear scale for several thermoplastic polymers.

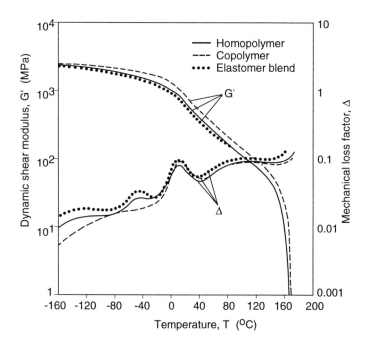

Figure 2.12   Elastic shear modulus and loss tangent for various polypropylene grades

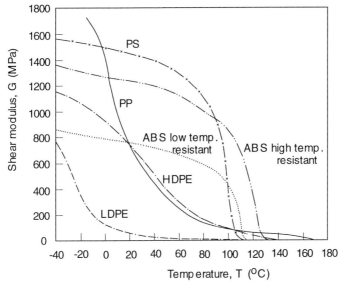

Figure 2.13 Elastic shear modulus for various polymers

SINUSOIDAL OSCILATORY TEST

If the test specimen in a sinusoidal oscillatory test is linearly elastic, the stress input and strain response would be in phase with the stress:

$$\tau(t) = \tau_0 \cos \omega t \qquad (2.12)$$

$$\gamma(t) = \gamma_0 \cos \omega t \qquad (2.13)$$

For an ideally viscous test specimen (Newtonian), the strain response lags $\frac{\pi}{2}$ radians behind the stress input:

$$\tau(t) = \tau_0 \cos \omega t \qquad (2.14)$$

$$\gamma(t) = \gamma_0 \cos\left(\omega t - \frac{\pi}{2}\right) \qquad (2.15)$$

Polymers behave somewhere in between these cases and their response is described by:

$$\tau(t) = \tau_0 \cos \omega t \quad \text{and} \qquad (2.16)$$

$$\gamma(t) = \gamma_0 \cos\left(\omega t - \delta\right) \qquad (2.17)$$

The shear modulus is complex

$$G^* = \frac{\tau(t)}{\gamma(t)} = \frac{\tau_0 e^{i\delta}}{\gamma_0} = \frac{\tau_0}{\gamma_0}(\cos\delta + i\sin\delta) = G' + G'' \qquad (2.18)$$

where G' is usually called the *storage modulus* and G'' is the *loss modulus*. The ratio of loss modulus to storage modulus is called the *loss tangent*:

$$\tan\delta = \frac{G''}{G'} \qquad (2.19)$$

Although the elastic shear modulus G' and the loss modulus, G'', are sufficient to characterize a material, one can also compute the logarithmic decrement, Δ, or loss factor by using

$$\Delta = \left(\frac{G''\pi}{G'}\right) \qquad (2.20)$$

The logarithmic decrement can also be written in terms of *loss tangent* $\tan\delta$, where δ is the mechanical loss angle. The loss tangent is then

$$\tan\delta = \frac{G''}{G'} = \frac{\Delta}{\pi} \qquad (2.21)$$

2.5 Mechanical Behavior of Filled and Reinforced Polymers

Fillers are materials intentionally inserted in polymers to make them stronger, lighter, electrically conductive or less expensive. Any filler affects the mechanical behavior of a polymetric material. For example, long fibers make the polymer stiffer but usually denser, whereas foaming makes it more compliant and much lighter. On the other hand, a filler such as calcium carbonate decreases the polymer's toughness, while making it considerably cheaper to produce.

Reinforced plastics are matrix polymers whose properties have been enhanced by introducing a reinforcement (fibers) of higher stiffness and strength. Such a material is usually called a *fiber reinforced polymer* (FRP) or a *fiber reinforced composite* (FRC). The purpose of introducing a fiber into a matrix is to transfer the load from the weaker material to the stronger one. This load transfer occurs over the length of the fiber as shown in Fig. 2.14.

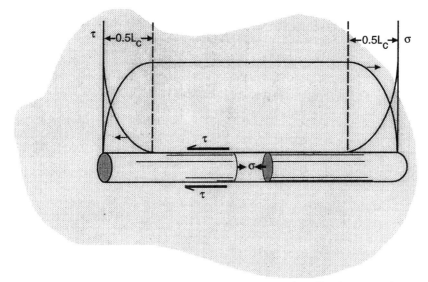

Figure 2.14   Schematic diagram of load transfer from matrix to fiber in a composite

The length to complete the load transfer from the matrix to the fiber, without fiber or matrix fracture, is usually called the critical length, L_c. For the specific case where there is perfect adhesion between fiber and matrix, experimental evidence suggests that aspect ratios of 100 or higher are required for maximum strength [15]. If composites have fibers that are shorter than their critical length they are referred to as *short fiber composites*. If the fibers are longer, they are called *long fiber composites* [16].

PROPERTIES OF FIBER REINFORCED COMPOSITES

Halpin and Tsai [17] developed a widely used model to predict the mechanical properties of aligned fiber reinforced composite laminates. With the notation in Fig. 2.15, where f and m represent the fiber and matrix, respectively; L the fiber length; D the fiber diameter; ϕ the volume fiber fraction, the longitudinal (L) and transverse (T) properties can be predicted using

$$E_L = E_m \left(\frac{1+\xi\eta\phi}{1-\eta\phi} \right) \tag{2.22}$$

$$E_T = E_m \left(\frac{1+\eta\phi}{1-\eta\phi} \right) \tag{2.23}$$

$$G_{LT} = G_m \left(\frac{1+\lambda\phi}{1-\lambda\phi} \right) = G_m \frac{v_{LT}}{v_m} \tag{2.24}$$

where,

$$\eta = \frac{\left(\frac{E_f}{E_m} - 1 \right)}{\left(\frac{E_f}{E_m} + \xi \right)} \tag{2.25}$$

$$\lambda = \frac{\left(\frac{G_f}{G_m} - 1 \right)}{\left(\frac{G_f}{G_m} + 1 \right)} \tag{2.26}$$

$$\xi = 2 \left(\frac{L}{D} \right) \tag{2.27}$$

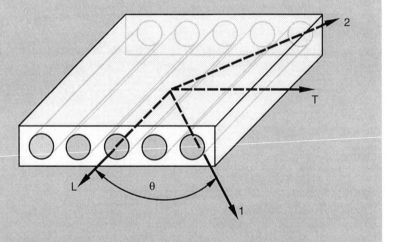

Figure 2.15   Schematic diagram of unidirectional, continuous fiber reinforced laminated structure

Most models accurately predict the longitudinal modulus as shown in Fig. 2.16 [18]. However, differences do exist between models when predicting the transverse modulus, as shown in Fig. 2.17 [18].

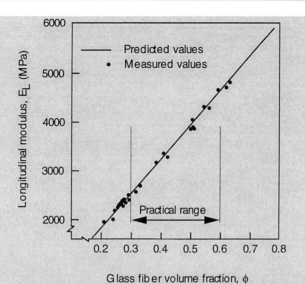

Figure 2.16 Measured and predicted longitudinal modulus for an unsaturated polyester/aligned glass fiber composite laminate as a function of volume fraction of glass content

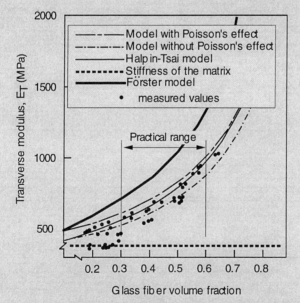

Figure 2.17 Measured and predicted transverse modulus for an unsaturated polyester/aligned glass fiber composite laminate as a function of volume fraction of glass content

Figure 2.18 [19] shows how the stiffness decreases as one rotates away from the longitudinal axis for an aligned fiber reinforced composite with different volume fraction fiber content.

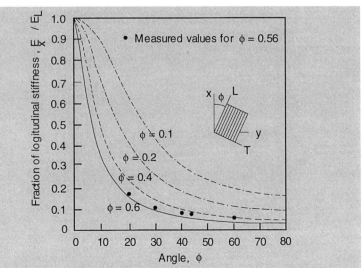

Figure 2.18 Measured and predicted elastic modulus in a uniderectional fiber reinforced laminate as a function of angle between loading and fiber direction

For high volume fraction fiber contents, only a slight misalignment of the fibers from the loading direction results in drastic property reductions.

The stiffness in a long fiber reinforced composite with a random planar orientation, such as encountered in sheet molding compound (SMC) charges, can be estimated using

$$E_{11} = E_{22} = E_{random} = \left[\frac{3}{8}\frac{1}{E_L} + \frac{3}{8}\frac{1}{E_T} - \frac{2}{8}\frac{\nu_{LT}}{E_L} + \frac{1}{8}\frac{1}{G_{LT}} \right]^{-1} \qquad (2.28)$$

2.6 Impact Strength

In practice, nearly all polymer components are subjected to impact loads. Since many polymers are tough and ductile, they are often well suited for this type of loading. However, under specific conditions even the most ductile materials, such as polypropylene, can fail in a brittle manner at low strains. These types of failure are prone to occur at low temperatures during high deformation rates.

According to several researchers [20, 21], a significantly high rate of deformation leads to complete embrittlement of polymers resulting in a lower threshold of elongation at break. Menges and Boden designed a special high speed elongational testing device to measure the minimum work required to break specimens. The minimum strain, ε_{min}, which can be measured with such a device, is a safe value to use in design calculations. One should always assume that if this minimum strain is exceeded anywhere in the component, initial fracture has already occurred. Table 2.1 [22, 23] presents minimum elongation at break values for selected thermoplastics on impact loading.

Table 2.1 Minimum Elongation at Break on Impact Loading

Polymer	ε_{min} (%)
HMW–PMMA	2.2
PA6 + 25% SFR	1.8
PP	1.8
uPVC	2.0
POM	4.0
PC + 20% SFR	4.0
PC	6.0

On the other hand, the stiffness and the stress at break of the material under consideration increases with the rate of deformation. Table 2.2 [22] presents data of the stress at break, σ_{min}, for selected thermoplastics on impact loading. This stress corresponds to the point where the minimum elongation at break has just been reached.

Table 2.2 Minimum Stress at Break on Impact Loading

Polymer	σ_{min} (MPa)
HMW-PMMA	135
PA6 + 25% Short fiber reinforced (SFR)	175
uPVC	125
POM	>130
PC + 20% SFR	>110
PC	>70

Figure 2.19 summarizes the stress-strain and fracture behavior of a HMW-PMMA tested at various rates of deformation. The area under the stress-strain curves represents the *volume-specific energy to fracture* (w). For impact, the elongation at break of 2.2% and the stress at break of 135 MPa represent a minimum of volume-specific energy because the stress increases with higher rates of deformation, but the elongation at break remains constant. Hence, if we assume a linear behavior, the *minimum volume-specific energy absorption* to fracture can be calculated using

$$w_{min} = 0.5 \, \sigma_{max} \, \varepsilon_{min} \qquad (2.29)$$

If the stress-strain distribution in the polymer component is known, one can estimate the minimum energy absorption capacity using w_{min}. It can be assumed that failure occurs if w_{min} is exceeded anywhere in the loaded component. This minimum volume-specific energy absorption, w_{min}, can be used as a design parameter. It can also be used for fiber reinforced polymeric materials [24].

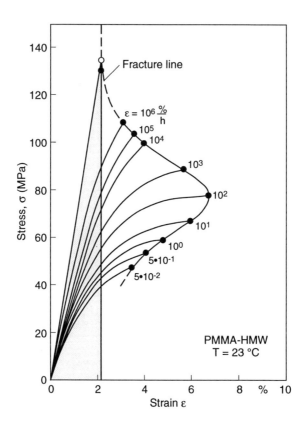

Figure 2.19   Stress-strain behavior of HMW-PMMA at various rates of deformation

2.7 Fatigue

Dynamic loading of any material that leads to failure after a certain number of cycles is called *fatigue* or *dynamic fatigue*. Dynamic fatigue is of extreme importance since a cyclic or fluctuating load causes a component to fail at much lower stresses than it does under monotonic loads.

Fatigue test results are plotted as stress amplitude versus number of cycles to failure. These graphs are usually called *S-N curves*, a term inherited from metal fatigue testing. Figure 2.20 [25] presents S-N curves for several thermoplastic and thermoset polymers tested at a 30 Hz frequency and about a zero mean stress, σ_m.

Fatigue in plastics is strongly dependent on the environment, the temperature, the frequency of loading, and surface finish. For example, bacause of surface irregularities and scratches, crack initiation at the surface is more likely in a polymer component that has been machined than in one that was injection molded. An injection molded article is formed by several layers of different orientation. In such parts, the outer layers act as a protective skin that inhibits crack initiation. In an injection molded part, cracks are more likely to initiate inside the component by defects such as weld lines and filler particles. The gate region is also a prime initiator of fatigue cracks. Corrosive environments also accelerate crack initiation and failure via fatigue.

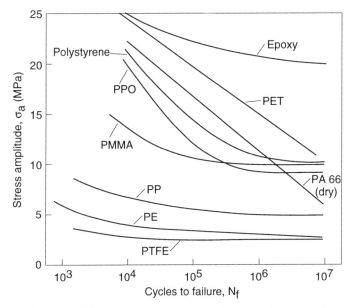

Figure 2.20   Stress-life (S-N) curves for several thermoplastic and thermoset polymers tested at a 30 Hz frequency about a zero mean stress

Temperature increases during testing is one of the main causes of failure when experimentally testing thermoplastic polymers under cyclic loads. The temperature rise during testing is caused by the combination of internal frictional or hysteretic heating and low thermal conductivity. At low frequency and stress, the temperature in the polymer specimen will rise and can eventually reach thermal equilibrium when the heat generated by hysteretic heating equals the heat removed from the specimen by conduction. As the frequency is increased, viscous heat is generated faster, causing the temperature to rise even further. After thermal equilibrium has been reached, a specimen eventually fails by conventional brittle fatigue, assuming the stress is above the endurance limit. However, if the frequency or stress level is increased even further, the temperature rises to the point that the test specimen softens and ruptures before reaching thermal equilibrium. This mode of failure is usually referred to as *thermal fatigue.*

2.8 Weathering

When exposed to the elements, polymeric materials can exhibit environmental cracks, which lead to failure at stress levels significantly lower than those without these environments. Ultraviolet radiation, moisture, and extreme temperatures harm the mechanical properties of plastic parts.

The strength losses and discoloration from weathering are mainly attributed to the ultra-violet rays in sunlight. This can be demonstrated by plotting properties as a function of sunlight exposure instead of total time exposed. Figure 2.21 [26] is a plot of percent of initial impact strength for an ABS as a function of sunlight exposure in three different locations, Florida, Arizona, and West Virginia. The curve reveals that by "normalizing" the curves with respect to exposure to sunshine, the three different sites with three completely different weather conditions lead to the same relationship between impact strength and sunlight exposure.

The effect of weathering can often be mitigated with pigments, such as TiO_2 or carbon black, which absorb ultraviolet radiation, preventing penetration through the polymer component surface.

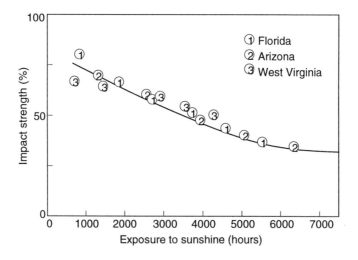

Figure 2.21   Impact strength of an ABS as a function of hours of actual sunlight exposure

Examples

2.1 For the poly-α-methylstyrene stress relaxation data in Fig.2.22 [27], create a master creep curve at T_g (204°C).

Identify the glassy, rubbery, viscous, and viscoelastic regions of the master curve. Identify each region with a spring-dashpot model diagram.

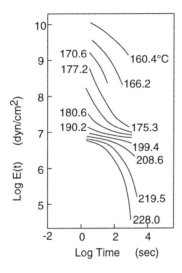

Figure 2.22 Stress relaxation data for poly-α-methylstyrene

The master creep curve for the above data is generated by sliding the individual relaxation curves horizontally until they match with their neighbors if the scale is fixed for a hypothetical curve at 204°C. Since a curve does not exist for the desired temperature, we can interpolate between 208.6°C and 199.4 °C. The resulting master curve is plotted on Fig.2.23. The amount each curve must be shifted to meet the master curve is the shift factor, Log a_T. Figure 2.24 represents the shift factor versus temperature. The solid line indicates the shift factor predicted by the WLF equation. Good agreement can be seen.

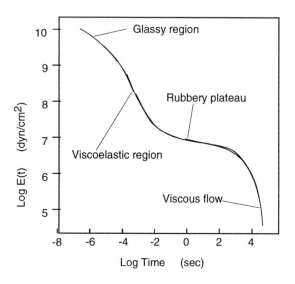

Figure 2.23 Master curve for poly-α-methylstyrene at 204°C

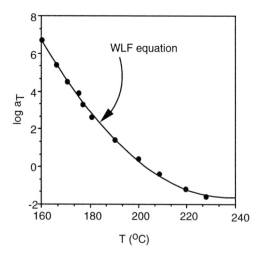

Figure 2.24 Shift factor and WLF for T_{ref}=204°C

Problems

2.1 Attached are some creep data for polystyrene at various temperatures [28]. Create a master curve at 109.8 °C by graphically sliding the curves at some temperatures horizontally until they line up.

Develop a plot of the shift factor, $\log(a_T)$ versus T, used to create your master curve. Compare your result with the WLF equation. The WLF equation is for a master curve at T_g (85 °C for this PS), but your master curve is for 109.8 °C, so be sure you make a fair comparison, such as shifting the results from the WLF equation, i.e., $(\text{Log}a_T)_{new} = \text{Log}a_T + K$.

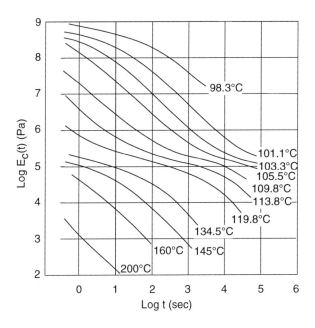

Figure 2.25 Creep modulus data for polystyrene.

2.2 Estimate the shear modulus constant, G_0, for the natural rubber (NR) and the styrene butadiene ruber-natural rubber compound (SBR/NR) presented in Fig. 2.4.

2.3 Generate 1 hour, 1 day, and 1 year isochronous (stress-strain) curves for polyacetal copolymer using the creep data presented below [3].

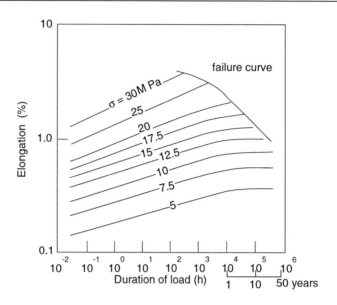

Figure 2.26 Creep data for polyacetal

2.4 What is the life expectancy of a polyacetal bracket with maximum bending stresses of 22 MPa ?

2.5 Generate a 2-year isochronous curve for the polypropylene curve presented in Fig. 2.8. Using this curve, estimate the thickness of a 50 mm diameter polypropylene pipe whose maximum allowable strain in a 2-year period should be 2%, while subjected to a 200 kPa internal pressure. Note: neglect the effect of biaxial state of stress.

2.6 Estimate the longitudinal modulus, E_L, transverse modulus, E_T, and shear modulus, G_{LT}, for a pultruded beam with unidirectional fibers. The matrix is an unsaturated polyester with $E_m = 2,500$ MPa and $v_m = 0.32$, and the fibers are glass with $E_f = 73,000$ MPa and $v_f = 0.25$.

2.7 Estimate the planar modulus of a compression molded automotive hood with the reinforcing fibers randomly oriented in the plane of the hood. The matrix is an unsaturated polyester with $E_m = 4,000$ MPa and $v_m = 0.32$, and the fibers are glass with $E_f = 73,000$ MPa and $v_f = 0.25$.

2.8 The PMMA presented in Fig. 2.19 will be used for an automotive stop light and subjected to impact loading. What is the minimum volume specific energy absorbed before fracture ?

References

1. Castiff, E. and A.V.J. Tobolsky, *Colloid Sci.* (1955), *10*, 375
2. Williams, M.L., R.F. Landel, and J.D. Ferry, *J. Amer. Chem. Soc.* (1955), 77, 3701
3. Domininghaus, H., *Plastics for Engineers*, Hanser Publishers (1993), Munich
4. Treloar, L.R.G., *The Physics of Rubber Elasticity*, 3rd. Ed. (1975), Clarendon Press, Oxford
5. Courtesy ICIPC, Medellín, Colombia.
6. Williams, M.L., R.F. Landel, and J.D. Ferry, *J. Amer. Chem. Soc.* (1955), 77, 3701
7. Guth, E., and R. Simha, *Kolloid-Zeitschrift* (1936), *74*, 266
8. Guth, E., *Proceedings of the American Physical Society*, (1937): *Physical Review* (1938), *53*, 321
9. Smallwood, H.M., *J. Appl. Phys.* (1944), *15*, 758
10. Mullins, L., and N.R. Tobin, *J. Appl. Polym. Sci.* (1965), *9*, 2993
11. ASTM, Plastics (II), 08.02, ASTM (1994), Philadelphia
12. Crawford, R.J., *Plastics Engineering*, 2nd ed., 47, Pergamon Press (1987), Oxford
13. Richard, K., E. Gaube and G. Diedrich, *Kunststoffe* (1959), *49*, 516
14. Gaube, E. and H.H. Kausch, *Kunststoffe* (1973), *63*, 391
15. Nielsen, L.E., and R.F. Landel, *Mechanical Properties of Polymers and Composites*, 2nd Ed., Marcel Dekker (1994), Inc., New York
16. Krishnamachari, S.I., *Applied Stress Analysis of Plastics*, Van Nostrand Reinhold (1993), New York
17. Tsai, S.W., J.C. Halpin, and N.J. Pagano, *Composite Materials Workshop*, Technomic Publishing Co. (1968), Stamford
18. Brintrup, H., Ph.D. Thesis (1974), IKV, RWTH-Aachen, Germany
19. Menges, G., *Kunststoffverarbeitung III*, 5, Lecture notes (1987), IKV, RWTH-Aachen
20. Boyer, R.F., *Polymer Eng. Sci.* (1968), *8, 161
21. Boden, H.E., Ph.D. Thesis (1983), IKV, RWTH-Aachen, Germany
22. Menges, G., and H.-E. Boden, *Failure of Plastics*, Chapter 9, Eds. W. Brostow, and R.D. Corneliussen, Hanser Publishers (1986), Munich
23. Andrews, E.H., *Fracture in Polymers* (1968), Oliver and Body, London
24. Rest, H., Ph.D. Thesis (1984), IKV-Aachen
25. Riddell, M.N., *Plast. Eng.*(1974), *40*, 4, 71
26. Ruhnke, G.M. and L.F. Biritz, *Kunststoffe* (1972), *62*, 250
27. Fujimoto, T., M. Ozaki and M. Nagasawa, *J. Polymer Sci.* (1968., 2, 6, 129
28. Pazek, D.J., *J. Polym. Sci.*(1968), A-2, (6), 621
29. Domininghaus, H., *Plastics for Engineers*, Hanser Publishers (1993), Munich.

3 Rheology of Polymer Melts

Rheology is the science of fluid behavior during flow induced deformation. Among the variety of materials that rheologists study, polymers have been found to be the most interesting and complex. Polymer melts are shear thinning and viscoelastic and their flow properties are temperature dependent. This chapter discusses the phenomena that are typical of polymer melts and covers the basic properties used to represent the flow behavior of polymers. The chapter also introduces rheometry. For further reading on rheology of polymer melts, consult references 1 to 6.

3.1 Introduction to Rheology

Viscosity is the most widely used material parameter when determining the behavior of polymers during processing. Since the majority of polymer processes are shear rate dominated, the viscosity of the melt is commonly measured using shear deformation measurement devices. For example, the simple shear flow generated in the sliding plate rheometer [7], shown in Fig. 3.1, exhibits a deviatoric stress defined by

$$\tau_{xy} = \eta(T, \dot{\gamma})\dot{\gamma}_{xy} \tag{3.1}$$

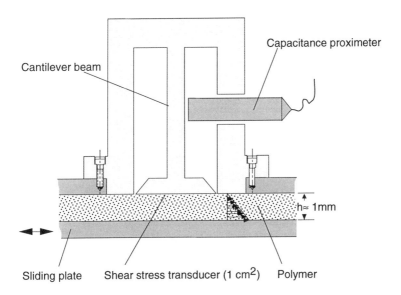

Figure 3.1. Schematic disgram of a sliding plate rheometer

where $\eta(T,\dot{\gamma})$ is the viscosity and $\dot{\gamma}_{xy}$ the shear rate defined by V/h. For the flow in Fig. 3.1, the magnitude of the rate of deformation tensor, $\dot{\gamma}$, is $\dot{\gamma}_{xy}$. There are also polymer processes, such as blow molding, thermoforming and fiber spinning, which are dominated by either elongation or by a combination of shear and elongational deformation. In addition, some polymer melts exhibit significant elastic effects during deformation.

3.1.1 Shear Thinning Behavior of Polymers

Most polymer melts are *shear thinning fluids*. The shear thinning effect is the reduction in viscosity at high rates of deformation, such as shown in Fig. 3.2 for an LDPE resin. This phenomenon occurs because at low rates of deformation, the polymer molecules are entangled and at high rates of deformation, the molecules are stretched out and disentangled. The disentangled molecules can slide past each other more easily, thus, lowering the bulk melt viscosity.

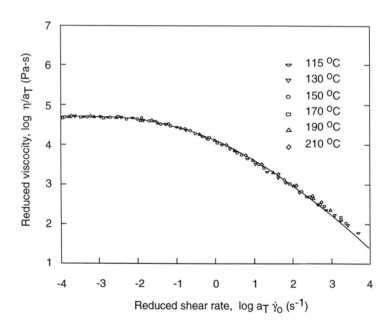

Figure 3.2   Reduced viscosity curve for an LDPE at a reference temperature of 150 °C

The power-law model proposed by Ostwald [8] and de Waale [9] is the simplest model that accurately represents the shear thinning region in the viscosity versus strain rate curve, but overshoots the Newtonian plateau at small strain rates. The power-law model is:

$$\eta = m(T)\dot{\gamma}^{n-1} \tag{3.2}$$

where m is called the *consistency index* and n the *power law index*. The consistency index may include the temperature dependence of the viscosity and can be represented as

$$m(T) = m_0 e^{-a(T-T_0)} \tag{3.3}$$

Power-law constants, as used in Eqs. (3.2) and (3.3), are presented in Table 3.1 for common thermoplastics.

Table 3.1   Power-Law Indices, Consistency Indices, and Temperature Dependence Constants for Common Thermoplastics

Polymer	m (Pa-s^n)	n	a (1/^{o}C)	T_0(^{o}C)
Polystyrene	2.80 x 10^4	0.28	-0.025	170
High density polyethylene	2.00 x 10^4	0.41	-0.002	180
Low density polyethylene	6.00 x 10^3	0.39	-0.013	160
Polypropylene	7.50 x 10^3	0.38	-0.004	200
Polyvinylchloride	1.70 x 10^4	0.26	-0.019	180

SIMPLIFIED FLOWS COMMON IN POLYMER PROCESSING

Many polymer processing operations can be modeled using simplified geometries and material models. This section presents several isothermal flows in simple geometries using a Newtonian viscosity and a power-law viscosity as described in Eq. (3.2).

Simple shear flow (Fig. 3.3)

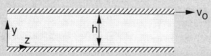

Figure 3.3 Schematic diagram of a simple shear flow

Simple shear flows are common in polymer processing, such as inside extruders as well as in certain coating flows. The flow field in simple shear is the same for all fluids and is described by

$$v_z(y) = v_0 \frac{y}{h} \tag{3.4}$$

$$Q = \frac{v_0 h W}{2} \tag{3.5}$$

Pressure flow through a slit (Fig. 3.4)

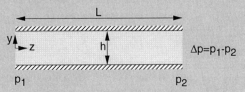

Figure 3.4 Schematic diagram of a pressure flow through a slit

The pressure flow through a slit is commonly encountered in flows through extrusion dies or inside injection molds. The Newtonian flow field is described using

$$v_z(y) = \left(\frac{h^2 \Delta p}{8 \mu L}\right) \left[1 - \left(\frac{2y}{h}\right)^2\right] \tag{3.6}$$

$$Q = \frac{W h^3 \Delta p}{12 \mu L} \tag{3.7}$$

When using the power law model (Eq. (3.2)) the flow field is described by

$$v_z(y) = \left(\frac{h}{2(s+1)}\right) \left(\frac{h \Delta p}{2 m L}\right)^s \left[1 - \left(\frac{2y}{h}\right)^{s+1}\right] \tag{3.8}$$

$$Q = \frac{W h^2}{2(s+2)} \left(\frac{h \Delta p}{2 m L}\right)^s$$

where s=1/n. (3.9)

Pressure flow through a tube - Hagen-Poiseuille flow (Fig. 3.5)

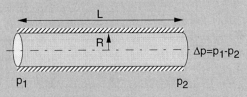

Figure 3.5 Schematic diagram of a tube flow

Pressure flow through a tube is encountered in the runner system in injection molds, in certain dies, and in the capillary rheometer. The Newtonian flow field is given by

$$v_z(r) = \frac{R^2 \Delta p}{4\mu L}\left[1 - \left(\frac{r}{R}\right)^2\right] \tag{3.10}$$

$$Q = \frac{\pi R^4 \Delta p}{8\mu L} \tag{3.11}$$

Using the power law fluid the flow field in a tube is described by

$$v_z(r) = \frac{R}{1+s}\left(\frac{R\Delta p}{2mL}\right)^s\left[1 - \left(\frac{r}{R}\right)^{s+1}\right] \tag{3.12}$$

$$Q = \left(\frac{\pi R^3}{s+3}\right)\left(\frac{R\Delta p}{2mL}\right)^s \tag{3.13}$$

Couette flow (Fig. 3.6)

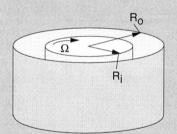

Figure 3.6 Schematic diagram of a Couette device

The Newtonian flow field in a Couette device is described by

$$v_\theta(r) = \frac{\Omega}{\kappa^2 - 1}\left(\frac{R_o^2 - r^2}{r}\right) \tag{3.14}$$

where $\kappa = R_0 / R_i$. Using the power-law model, the flow field inside a Couette device is described by

$$v_\theta(r) = \frac{\Omega}{\kappa^{2s} - 1}\left(\frac{R_o^{2s} - r^{2s}}{r^{2s-1}}\right) \tag{3.15}$$

NON-ISOTHERMAL FLOWS IN POLYMER PROCESSING

Although we simplify analyses of polymer processes by assuming isothermal conditions, most operations are non-isothermal since they include melting and viscous dissipation. Hence, the temperature of the polymer melt lies between T_g (or T_m) and the heater temperature, T_h., and often exceeds T_h due to viscous dissipation. An estimate the maximum temperature rise due to viscous heating in a simple shear flow is

$$\Delta T_{max} = \frac{\eta V_0^2}{8k} \tag{3.16}$$

To estimate if viscous dissipation is important in a polymer process, the Brinkman number, Br, is often used

$$Br = \frac{\eta V_0^2}{k(T_h - T_g)} \tag{3.17}$$

The Brinkman number is the ratio of the heat generated via viscous dissipation and the heat transport via conduction. The choice of temperature difference, e.g. $(T_h - T_g)$, depends on the type of problem being analyzed.

3.1.2 Normal Stresses in Shear Flow

The tendency of polymer molecules to "curl-up" while they are being stretched in shear flow results in normal stresses in the fluid. For example, the shear flow presented in Eq. (3.1) has measurable normal stress differences, N_1 and N_2, which are called the *first* and *second normal stress differences*, respectively. The first and second normal stress differences are material dependent and are defined by

$$N_1 = \tau_{xx} - \tau_{yy} = -\Psi_1(\dot{\gamma},T)\, \dot{\gamma}_{xy}^2 \tag{3.18}$$

$$N_2 = \tau_{yy} - \tau_{zz} = -\Psi_2(\dot{\gamma},T)\, \dot{\gamma}_{xy}^2 \tag{3.19}$$

The material functions, Ψ_1 and Ψ_2, are called the primary and secondary normal stress coefficients, and are also functions of the magnitude of the strain rate tensor and temperature. The first and second normal stress differences do not change sign when the direction of the strain rate changes. This is reflected in Eqs. (3.18) and (3.19). Figure 3.7 [10] presents the first normal stress difference coefficient for the LDPE melt of Fig. 3.2 at a reference temperature of 150 °C. The second normal stress difference is difficult to measure and is often approximated by

$$\Psi_2(\dot{\gamma}) \approx -0.1\Psi_1(\dot{\gamma}) \tag{3.20}$$

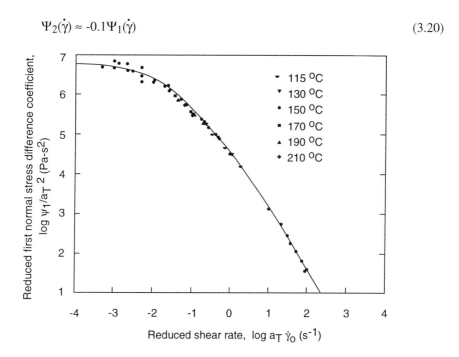

Figure 3.7   Reduced first normal stress difference coefficient for an LDPEmelt at a reference temperature of 150 °C

The normal stress differences play significant roles during processing. For example, the first normal stress difference is partly responsible for *extrudate swell* (Fig. 3.8) at the exit of the die. The second normal stress differences help diminish the eccentricity of a wire in the die during the wire coating process [11].

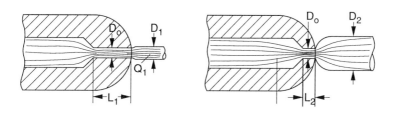

Figure 3.8   Schematic diagram of extrudate swell during extrusion

3.1.3 Deborah Number

A useful parameter for estimating the elastic effects during flow is the Deborah number:

$$De = \frac{\lambda}{t_p} \tag{3.21}$$

where λ is the relaxation time of the polymer and t_p is a characteristic process time. The characteristic process time can be defined by the ratio of characteristic die dimension and average speed through the die. A Deborah number of zero represents a viscous fluid and a Deborah number of ∞, an elastic solid. As the Deborah number exceeds one, the polymer does not have enough time to relax during the process, resulting in *extrudate swell* [*], *shark skin* or even *melt fracture*.

Although many factors affect the amount of extrudate swell, fluid "memory" and normal stress effects are most significant. However, abrupt changes in boundary conditions, such as the separation point of the extrudate from the die, also play a role in the swelling or cross section reduction of the extrudate. In practice, the fluid memory contribution to die swell can be mitigated by lengthening the land length of the die. This is schematically depicted in Fig. 3.8. A long die land separates the polymer from the manifold long enough to allow it to "forget" its past shapes.

Waves in the extrudate may also appear as a result of high speeds during extrusion, where the polymer cannot relax. This phenomenon is generally called *shark skin* and is shown for an HDPE in Fig. 3.9-a [12]. Polymers can be extruded at such high speeds that an intermittent separation of melt and inner die walls occurs as shown in Fig. 3.9-b. This phenomenon is often called *stick-slip* or *spurt flow* and is attributed to high shear stresses between the polymer and the die wall. This phenomenon occurs when the shear stress is near the critical value of 0.1 MPa [13-15]. If the speed is further increased, a helical geometry is extruded as shown for a polypropylene extrudate in Fig. 3.9-c. Eventually, the speeds are so high that a chaotic pattern develops such as the one shown in Fig. 3.9-d. This well known phenomenon is called *melt fracture*. Shark skin is frequently absent, and spurt flow seems to occur only with linear polymers.

The critical shear stress has been reported to be independent of the melt temperature but inversely proportional to the weight average molecular weight [15,16]. However, Vinogradov et al. [13] presented results where the critical stress was independent of molecular weight except at low molecular weights. Dealy and co-workers [15] and Denn [17] give an extensive overview of various melt fracture phenomena. Both references are recommended.

---

[*] Newtonian fluids, which do not experience elastic or normal stress effects, also show some extrudate swell or reduction. A Newtonian fluid extruded at high shear rates reduces its cross section to 87% of the diameter of the die. This swell is the result of inertia effects caused by the rearrangement from the parabolic velocity distribution inside the die to the flat velocity distribution of the extrudate. If the polymer is extruded at very low shear rates it swells to 113% of the diameter of the die.

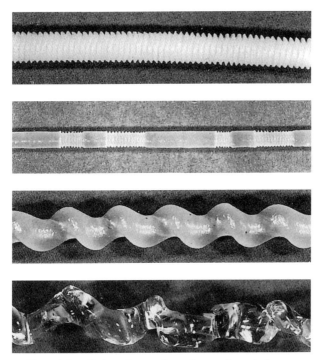

Figure 3.9   Various shapes of extrudates under melt fracture

SONG OF DEBORAH

M. Reiner is credited with naming the Deborah Number after the song of Deborah, Judges 5:5- "The mountains flowed before the Lord"(Fig. 3.10). It was first mentioned in his article "The Deborah Number" in the January 1964 issue of Physics Today.

Figure. 3.10 Nestles Canyon, Arizona. Courtesy of Wolfgang Cohnen (©1997)

3.1.4 Rheology of Curing Thermosets

A curing thermoset polymer has a conversion or cure dependent viscosity that increases as the molecular weight of the reacting polymer increases. For the vinyl ester whose curing history is shown in Fig. 3.11 [19], the viscosity behaves as shown in Fig. 3.12 [17]. Hence, a complete model for viscosity of a reacting polymer must contain the effects of strain rate, $\dot{\gamma}$, temperature, T, and degree of cure, c, such as

$$\eta = \eta(\dot{\gamma}, T, c) \tag{3.22}$$

There are no generalized models that include all these variables for thermosetting polymers. However, extensive work has been done on the viscosity of polyurethanes [19, 20] used in the reaction injection molding process. An empirical relation which models the viscosity of these mixing activated polymers, given as a function of temperature and degree of cure, is written as

$$\eta = \eta_0 \, e^{E/RT} \left(\frac{c_g}{c_g - c} \right)^{C_1 + C_2 c} \tag{3.23}$$

where E is the activation energy of the polymer, R is the ideal gas constant, T is the temperature, c_g is the gel point , c the degree of cure, and C_1 and C_2 are constants that fit the experimental data. The gel point is the degree of cure when the molecular weight goes to infinity or when the molecules become interconnected.

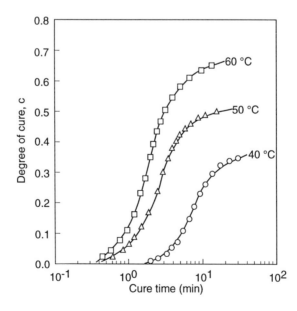

Figure 3.11   Degree of cure as a function of time for a vinyl ester at various isothermal cure temperatures

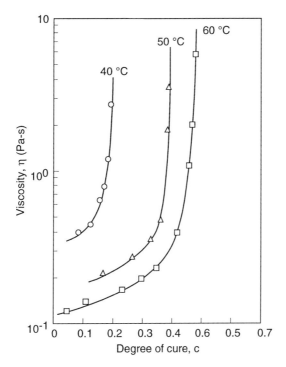

Figure 3.12   Viscosity as a function of degree of cure for a vinyl ester at various isothermal cure temperatures

3.1.5 Suspension Rheology

Particles suspended in a material, such as in filled or reinforced polymers, have a direct effect on the properties of the final article and on the viscosity during processing. The model which best fits experimental data is the one given by Guth [21]:

$$\frac{\eta f}{\eta 0} = 1 + 2.5\phi + 14.1\phi^2 \tag{3.24}$$

Figure 3.13 compares experimental data to Guth's equation. The experiments were performed on polyethylene and polystyrene containing different fill factors of spherical glass particles ranging between 36 μm and 99.8 μm in diameter. The model agrees well with the experimental data up to volume fractions of 30%.

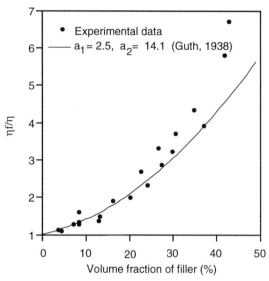

Figure 3.13   Viscosity increase as a function of volume fraction of filler for polystyrene and LDPE.

VISCOELASTIC FLOW MODELS

Viscoelasticity has already been introduced in Chapter 2 based on linear viscoelasticity. However, in polymer processing large deformations are imposed on the material, requiring the use of non-linear viscoelastic models. There are two types of general non-linear viscoelastic flow models, the differential model and the integral model.

An overview of numerical simulation of viscoelastic flow systems and an extensive literature review on the subject was given by Keunings [22], and detail on numerical implementation of viscoelastic models are given by Crochet et al. [23] and Debbaut et al. [24]. As an example of the application of differential models to predict flow of polymeric liquids, Dietsche and Dooley [25], recently evaluated the White–Metzner, the Phan-Thien Tanner-1 and the Giesekus models by comparing finite element and experimental results of the flow inside multi-layered coextrusion dies. Figure 3.14 [26] presents the progression of a matrix of dyed circular polystyrene strands flowing in an identical polystyrene matrix down a channel with a square cross section of 0.95 x 0.95 cm. The cuts in the figure are shown at intervals of 7.6 cm. The circulation pattern caused by the secondary normal stress differences inside non-circular dies were captured well by the Phan-Thien Tanner and Giesekus models but, as expected, not by the White–Metzner model. Figure 3.14 also presents flow patterns predicted by the Phan-Thien Tanner model. The shape of the circulation patterns were predicted accurately. The flow simulation of the square die predicted a velocity on the order of 10^{-5} m/s along the diagonal of the cross section, which agreed with the experimental results. Also, Baaijens [27], recently evaluated the Phan-Thien Tanner models 1 and 2, and the Giesekus models. He compared finite element results to measured isochromatic birefringence patterns using complex experiments with polymer melts and solutions. His simulation results predicted the general shape of the measured birefringence patterns. He found that at high Deborah numbers, the Phan-Thien Tanner models converged more easily than the Giesekus model.

Figure 3.14 Simulated flow patterns and polystyrene strand profile progression in a square die

3.2 Rheometry

In industry, there are various ways to qualify and quantify the properties of the polymer melt. The techniques range from simple analyses for checking the consistency of the material at certain conditions, to more difficult fundamental measurements to evaluate viscosity and normal stress differences. This section includes three such techniques to give the reader a general idea of current measuring methods.

3.2.1 The Melt Flow Indexer

The melt flow indexer is often used in industry to characterize a polymer melt and as a simple and quick means of quality control. It takes a single point measurement using standard testing conditions specific to each polymer class on a ram type extruder or extrusion plastometer as shown in Fig. 3.15. The standard procedure for testing the flow rate of thermoplastics using a extrusion plastometer is described in the ASTM D1238 test [28]. During the test, a sample is heated in the barrel and extruded from a short cylindrical die using a piston actuated by a weight. The weight of the polymer in grams extruded during the 10-minute test is the melt flow index (MFI) of the polymer.

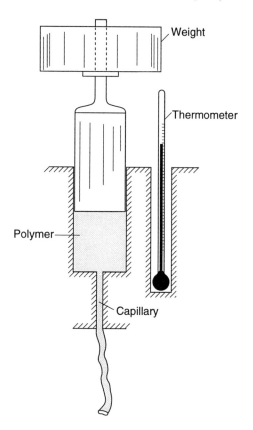

Figure 3.15   Schematic diagram of an extrusion plastometer used to measure melt flow index

3.2.2 The Capillary Viscometer

The most common and simplest device for measuring viscosity is the capillary visco-meter. Its main component is a straight tube or capillary, and it was first used to measure the viscosity of water by Hagen [29] and Poiseuille [30]. A capillary rheometer has a pressure driven flow for which the shear rate is maximum at the wall and zero at the center of the flow, making it a non-homogeneous flow.

Since pressure driven viscometers employ heterogeneous flows, they can only measure steady shear functions such as viscosity, $\eta(\dot{\gamma})$. However, they are widely used because they are relatively inexpensive and simple to operate. Despite their simplicity, long capillary viscometers give the most accurate viscosity data available. Another major advantage is that the capillary rheometer has no free surfaces in the test region, unlike other types of rheometers such as the cone and plate rheometer, discussed next. When the strain rate dependent viscosity of polymer melts is measured, capillary rheometers are capable of obtaining such data at shear rates greater than 10 s^{-1}. This is important for processes with higher rates of deformation like mixing, extrusion, and injection molding. Because its design is basic and it only needs a pressure head at its entrance, the capillary rheometer can easily attach to the end of a screw- or ram-type extruder for online measurements. This makes the capillary viscometer an efficient tool for industry. The basic features of the capillary rheometer are shown in Fig. 3.16.

VISCOSITY FROM CAPILLARY VISCOMETER DATA

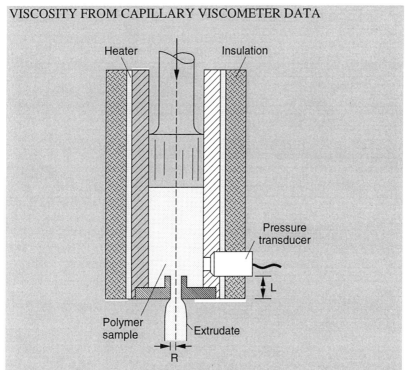

Figure 3.16   Schematic diagram of a capillary viscometer

A capillary tube of radius R and length L is connected to the bottom of a reservoir. Pressure drop and flow rate through this tube are used to determine the viscosity. At the wall, the shear stress is:

$$\tau_w = \frac{R}{2}\frac{(P_0 - P_L)}{L} = \frac{R}{2}\frac{\Delta p}{L} \tag{3.25}$$

Equation (3.25) requires that the capillary be long enough to assure fully developed flow, where end effects are insignificant. However, because of entrance effects, the actual pressure profile along the length of the capillary exhibits curvature. The effect is shown schematically in Fig. 3.17 [31] and was corrected by Bagley [32] using the end correction e:

$$\tau_w = \frac{1}{2} \frac{(P_0 - P_L)}{(L/R + e)}.$$ (3.26)

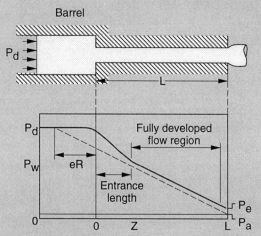

Figure 3.17   Entrance effects in a typical capillary viscometer

The correction e at a specific shear rate can be found by plotting pressure drop for various capillary L/D ratios as shown in Fig. 3.18 [31].

The equation for shear stress is then

$$\tau_{rz} = \frac{r}{R}\tau_w.$$ (3.27)

To obtain the shear rate at the wall the Weissenberg–Rabinowitsch [33] equation can be used

$$\dot{\gamma}_w = \frac{1}{4}\dot{\gamma}_{aw}\left(3 + \frac{d(\ln Q)}{d(\ln \tau)}\right)$$ (3.28)

where, $\dot{\gamma}_{aw}$ is the apparent or Newtonian shear rate at the wall and is written as

$$\dot{\gamma}_{aw} = \frac{4Q}{\pi R^3}$$ (3.29)

The shear rate and shear stress at the wall are now known. Therefore, using the measured values of the flow rate, Q, and the pressure drop, $p_o - p_L$, the viscosity is calculated using

$$\eta = \frac{\tau_w}{\dot{\gamma}_w}. \tag{3.30}$$

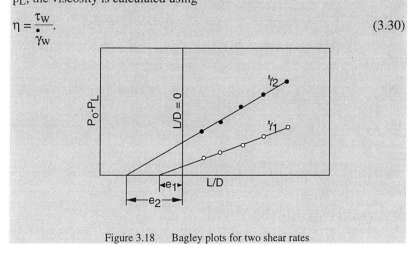

Figure 3.18   Bagley plots for two shear rates

3.2.3 The Cone-and-Plate Rheometer

The cone-and-plate rheometer is another rheological measuring device widely accepted in the polymer industry. Here, a disk of polymer is squeezed between a plate and a cone as shown in Fig. 3.19. When the disk is rotated, the torque and the rotational speed are related to the viscosity, and the force required to keep the cone at the plate is related to the first normal stress difference. The secondary normal stress difference is related to the pressure distribution along the radius of the plate.

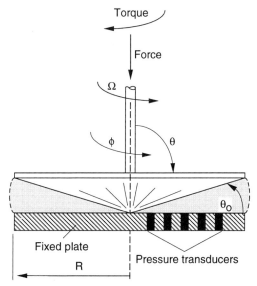

Figure 3.19   Schematic diagram of a cone-plate rheometer

Examples

3.1 Derive the equation that describes the pressure driven velocity field inside a tube of constant diameter (Eq. (3.10)).

In our solution scheme, we must first choose a coodinate system:

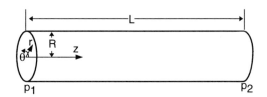

Next we must state our assumption:

- no variations in the θ direction: $\dfrac{\partial}{\partial \theta} = v_\theta = 0$,

- steady state: $\dfrac{\partial}{\partial t} = 0$,

- no velocity in the radial direction: $v_r = 0$.

The continuity equation (Appendix 6) reduces to

$$\frac{\partial v_z}{\partial z} = 0$$

Using the reduced continuity equation and the above assumptions, then only the z-component of the equation of motion (Appendix 6) is needed

$$0 = -\frac{\partial p}{\partial z} + \mu \left[\frac{1}{r}\frac{\partial}{\partial r}\left(r \frac{\partial v_z}{\partial r} \right) \right]$$

letting $\dfrac{\partial p}{\partial z} = \dfrac{\Delta p}{L}$ and integrating gives

$$r \frac{\partial v_z}{\partial r} = \frac{r^2}{2\mu}\left(\frac{\Delta p}{L} \right) + C_1$$

Since $\dfrac{\partial v_z}{\partial r} = 0$ at $r = 0$, $C_1 = 0$. Integrating again, we get

$$v_z = \frac{r^2}{4\mu}\left(\frac{\Delta p}{L}\right) + C_2$$

Since $v_z = 0$ at $r = R$, the above equation becomes

$$v_z = \frac{R^2 \Delta p}{4\mu L}\left[1 - \left(\frac{r}{R}\right)^2\right]$$

Problems

3.1 A single screw extruder can be modeled using a combination of shear flow (Fig. 3.3) and pressure flow between parallel plates (Fig. 3.4). Estimate the volumetric flow rate, Q, as a function of die pressure, Δp, with a Newtonian fluid assumption, using the notation in Fig.4.5 of the extrusion chapter.

3.2 Estimate the consistency index, m_0, and the power-law index, n, for the LDPE presented in Fig. 3.2.

3.3 Derive the equation that predicts the volumetric throughput during pressure flow through a slit (Eq. (3.7)).

3.4 Derive the the the Hagen-Poiseuille equation for a power law fluid (Eq. (3.13)).

3.5 You are to extrude a polystyrene sheet through a die with a land length of 0.1 meters. What is the maximum speed you can extrude the sheet if the relaxation time of the polystyrene is 0.5 seconds for the given processing temperature ?

References

1.   Macosko, C.W., *Rheology: Principles, Measurements and Applications*, VCH (1994), New York
2.   Dealy, J.M., and K.F. Wissbrun, *Melt Rheology and Its Role in Plastics Processing*, Van Nostrand (1990), New York
3.   Tanner, R.I., *Engineering Rheology*, Clarendon Press (1985), Oxford
4.   Bird, R.B., R.C. Armstrong, and O. Hassager, *Dynamics of Polymeric Liquids*, 2nd Ed., Vol.1, John Wiley & Sons (1987), New York
5.   Gordon, G.V., and M.T. Shaw, *Computer Programs for Rheologists*, Hanser Publishers (1994), Munich
6.   Bird, R.B., and J.M. Wiest, *Annu. Rev. Fluid Mech.* (1995), *27*, 169
7.   Giacomin, A.J., T. Samurkas, and J.M. Dealy, *Polym. Eng. Sci.* (1989), *29*, 499

8.   Ostwald, W., *Kolloid-Z.* (1925), 36, 99
9.   de Waale, A., *Oil and Color Chem. Assoc. Journal* (1923), 6, 33
10. Laun, H.M., *Rheol. Acta* (1978), *17*,1
11. Tadmor, Z., and R.B. Bird, *Polym. Eng. Sci.* (1974), *14*, 124
12. Agassant, J.-F., P. Avenas, J.-Ph. Sergent, and P.J. Carreau, *Polymer Processing: Principles and Modeling*, Hanser Publishers (1991), Munich
13. Vinogradov, G.V., A.Y., Malkin, Y.G. Yanovskii, E.K. Borisenkova, B.V. Yarlykov, and G.V. Berezhnaya, *J. Polym. Sci. Part A-2* (1972), *10*, 1061
14. Vlachopoulos, J., and M. Alam, *Polym. Eng. Sci.* (1972), *12*, 184
15. Hatzikiriakos, S.G., and J.M. Dealy, *ANTEC Tech. Papers* (1991), *37*, 2311
16. Spencer, R.S., and R.D. Dillon, *J. Colloid Inter. Sci.* (1947), *3*, 163
17. Denn, M.M., *Annu. Rev. Fluid Mech.* (1990), *22*, 13
18. Han, C.D. and K.W. Lem, *J. Appl. Polym. Sci.* (1984), *29*, 1879
19. Castro, J.M. and C.W. Macosko, *AIChe J.* (1982), *28*, 250
20. Castro, J.M., S.J. Perry and C.W. Macosko, *Polymer Comm.* (1984), *25*, 82
21. Guth, E., and R. Simha, Kolloid-Zeitschrift (1936), 74, 266
22. Keunings, R., *Simulation of Viscoelastic Fluid Flow*, in *Computer Modeling for Polymer Processing*, Ed. C.L. Tucker III, Hanser Publishers (1989), Munich
23. Crocket, MJ., A.R., Davies, and K. Walters, *Numerical Simulation of Non-Newtonian Flow*, Elsevier (1984), Amsterdam
24. Debbaut, B., J.M. Marchal, and M.J. Crochet, *J. Non-Newtonian Fluid Mech.* (1988), *29*, 119
25. Dietsche, L., and J. Dooley, *SPE ANTEC* (1995), *53*, 188
26. Dooley, J., and K. Hughes, *SPE ANTEC* (1995), *53*, 69
27. Baaijens, J.P.W., *Evaluation of Constitutive Equations for Polymer Melts and Solutions in Complex Flows*, Ph.D. Thesis (1994), Eidhoven University of Technology, Eidhoven, The Netherlands
28. ASTM, 8.01, Plastics (I), ASTM (1994), Philadelphia
29. Hagen, G.H.L., *Annalen der Physik* (1839), *46*, 423
30. Poiseuille, L.J., *Comptes Rendus 11* (1840), 961
31. Dealy, J.M., *Rheometers for Molten Plastics*, Van Nostrand Reinhold Company (1982), New York
32. Bagley, E.B., *J. Appl. Phys.* (1957), *28*, 624
33. Rabinowitsch, B., *Z. Phys. Chem.* (1929), *145*, 1

4 Extrusion

During extrusion, a polymer melt is pumped through a shaping die and formed into a profile. This profile can be a plate, a film, a tube, or have any shape for its cross section. Ram-type extruders were first built by J. Bramah in 1797 to extrude seamless lead pipes. The first ram-type extruders for rubber were built by Henry Bewley and Richard Brooman in 1845. In 1846 a patent for cable coating was filed for trans-gutta-percha and cis-hevea rubber and the first insulated wire was laid across the Hudson River for the Morse Telegraph Company in 1849. The first screw extruder was patented by Mathew Gray in 1879 for the purpose of wire coating. However, the screw pump can be attributed to Archimedes, and the actual invention of the screw extruder in polymer processing by A.G. DeWolfe of the United States dates to the early 1860s. The first extrusion of thermoplastic polymers was done at the Paul Troester Maschinenfabrik in Hannover, Germany in 1935.

Although ram and screw extruders are both used to pump highly viscous polymer melts through passages to generate specified profiles, they are based on different principles. The schematic in Fig. 4.1 shows under what principles ram extruders, screw extruders, and other pumping systems work.

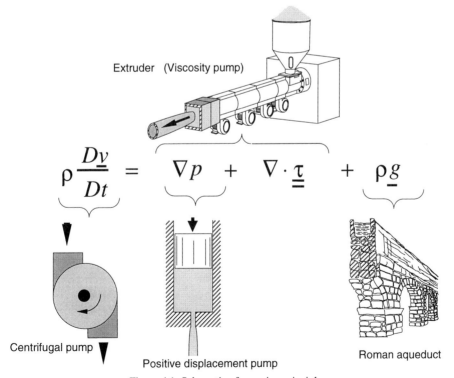

Extruder (Viscosity pump)

$$\rho \frac{Dv}{Dt} = \nabla p + \nabla \cdot \underline{\underline{\tau}} + \rho \underline{g}$$

Centrifugal pump

Positive displacement pump

Roman aqueduct

Figure 4.1 Schematic of pumping principles

The ram extruder is a positive displacement pump based on the pressure gradient term of the equation of motion. Here, as the volume is reduced, the fluid is displaced from one point to the other, resulting in a pressure rise. The gear pump, widely used in the polymer processing industry, also works on this principle. On the other hand, a screw extruder is a *viscosity pump* that works based on the pressure gradient term and the deformation of the fluid, represented as the divergence of the deviatoric stress tensor in Fig. 4.1. The centrifugal pump, based on the fluid inertia, and the Roman aqueduct, based on the potential energy of the fluid, are also represented in the figure and are typical of low viscosity liquids.

In today's polymer industry, the most commonly used extruder is the single screw extruder, schematically depicted in Fig. 4.2. The single screw extruder can either have a smooth inside barrel surface, called a *conventional single screw extruder*, or a grooved feed zone, called a *grooved feed extruder*. In some cases, an extruder can have a degasing zone, required to extract moisture, volatiles, and other gases that form during the extrusion process.

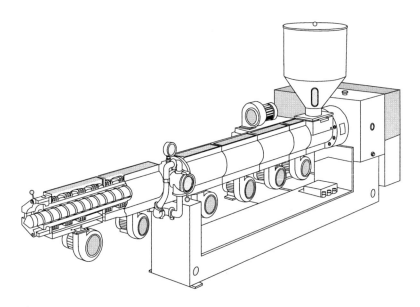

Figure 4.2 Schematic of a single screw extruder (Reifenhäuser)

Another important class of extruders are the twin screw extruders, schematically depicted in Fig. 4.3. Twin screw extruders can have co-rotating or counter-rotating screws, and the screws can be intermeshing or non-intermeshing. Twin screw extruders are primarily employed as mixing and compounding devices, as well as polymerization reactors. The mixing aspects of single and twin screw extruders are detailed in Chapter 5.

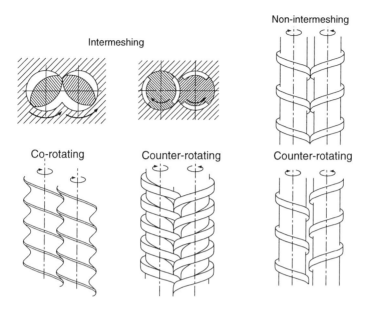

Figure 4.3. Schematic of different twin screw extruders

4.1 The Plasticating Extruder

The plasticating single screw extruder is the most common equipment in the polymer industry. It can be part of an injection molding unit and found in numerous other extrusion processes, including blow molding, film blowing, and wire coating. A schematic of a plasticating or three-zone, single screw extruder, with its most important elements, is in Fig. 4.4. Table 4.1 presents typical extruder dimensions and relationships common in single screw extruders.

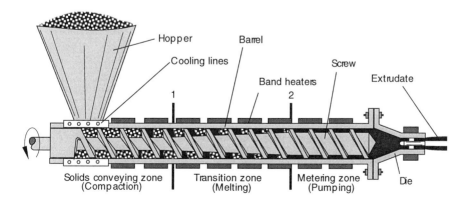

Figure 4.4 Schematic of a plasticating single screw extruder

Table 4.1 Typical extruder dimensions and relationships (the notation for Table 4.1 is defined in Fig. 4.5.)

L/D	Length to Diameter ratio
	20 or less for feeding or melt extruders
	25 for blow molding, film blowing and injection molding
	30 or higher for vented extruders or high output extruders
D	Standard diameter
U.S. (inches)	0.75, 1.0, 1.5, 2, 2.5, 3.5, 4.5, 6, 8, 10, 12, 14, 16, 18, 20, and 24
Europe (mm)	20, 25, 30, 35, 40, 50, 60, 90, 120, 150, 200, 250, 300, 350, 400, 450, 500, and 600
ϕ	Helix angle
	17.65° for a square pitch screw where $L_s=D$
	New trend: $0.8 < L_s/D < 1.2$
h	Channel depth in the metering section
	$(0.05\text{-}0.07)D$ for D<30 mm
	$(0.02\text{-}0.05)D$ for D>30 mm
β	Compression ratio: $h_{feed} = \beta h$
	2 to 4
δ	Clearance between the screw flight and the barrel
	0.1 mm for D<30 mm
	0.15 mm for D>30 mm
N	Screw speed
	1-2 rev/s (60-120 rpm) for large extruders
	1-5 rev/s (60-300 rpm) for small extruders
V_b	Barrel velocity (relative to screw speed) = πDN
	0.5 m/s for most polymers
	0.2 m/s for unplasticized PVC
	1.0 m/s for LDPE

The plasticating extruder can be divided into three main zones:

- The solids conveying zone
- The melting or transition zone
- The metering or pumping zone

The tasks of a plasticating extruder are to:

- Transport the solid pellets or powder from the hopper to the screw channel
- Compact the pellets and move them down the channel
- Melt the pellets
- Mix the polymer into a homogeneous melt
- Pump the melt through the die

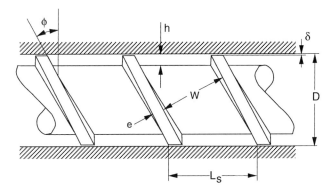

Figure 4.5 Schematic diagram of a screw section

The pumping capability and characteristic of an extruder can be represented with sets of *die and screw characterisctic curves*. Figure 4.6 presents such curves for a conventional (smooth barrel) single screw extruder.

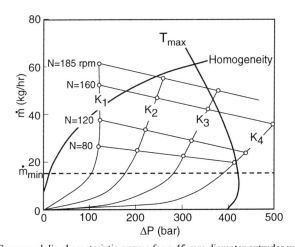

Figure 4.6 Screw and die characteristic curves for a 45 mm diameter extruder with an LDPE

The die characteristic curves are labelled K_1, K_2, K_3, and K_4 in ascending order of die restriction. Here, K_1 represents a low resistance die such as for a thick plate, and K_4 represents a restrictive die, such as is used for film. The different screw characteristic curves represent different screw rotational speeds. In a screw characteristic curve the point of maximum throughput and no pressure build-up is called the point of *open discharge*. This occurs when there is no die. The point of maximum pressure build-up and no throughput is called the point of *closed discharge*. This occurs when the extruder is plugged.

Shown in Fig. 4.6 are also lines that represent critical aspects encountered during extrusion. The curve labeled T_{max} represents the conditions at which excessive temperatures are reached as a result of viscous heating. The feasibility line ($\dot{m}_{min}$) represents the throughput required to have an economically feasible system. The processing conditions to the right of the homogeneity line render a thermally and physically heterogeneous polymer melt.

4.1.1 The Solids Conveying Zone

The task of the solids conveying zone is to move the polymer pellets or powders from the hopper to the screw channel. Once the material is in the screw channel, it is compacted and transported down the channel. The process to compact the pellets and to move them can only be accomplished if the friction at the barrel surface exceeds the friction at the screw surface. This can be visualized if one assumes the material inside the screw channel to be a nut sitting on a screw. As we rotate the screw without applying outside friction, the nut (polymer pellets) rotates with the screw without moving in the axial direction. As we apply outside forces (barrel friction), the rotational speed of the nut is less than the speed of the screw, causing it to slide in the axial direction. Virtually, the solid polymer is then "unscrewed" from the screw.

ANALYSIS OF SOLIDS CONVEYING ZONE

The most complete analysis of the solids conveying zone in single screw extruders was performed by Darnell and Mol [1] and continued by Tadmor and Klein [2].

A useful limiting case is when the friction on the screw surface is negligible compared to the friction on the barrel, and when the pressure build-up in the screw channel is negligible (open discharge). These assumptions lead to a maximum mass throughput of

$$\dot{m} = \rho_{bulk} \pi D_b N \tan \phi \left(\frac{\pi}{4} \left(D_b^2 - D_s^2 \right) - \frac{e h_{feed}}{\sin \phi} \right) \tag{4.1}$$

To maintain a high coefficient of friction between the barrel and the polymer, the feed section of the barrel must be cooled, usually with cold water cooling lines. The frictional forces also result in a pressure rise in the feed section. This pressure compresses the solids bed which continues to travel in down the channel as it melts in the transition zone. Figure 4.6 presents the pressure build-up in a conventional, smooth barrel extruder. In these extruders, most of the pressure required for pumping and mixing is generated in the metering section.

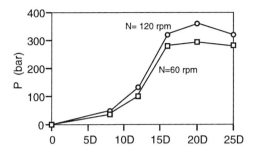

Figure 4.7 Conventional extruder pressure distribution

The simplest mechanism for ensuring high friction between the polymer and the barrel surface is grooving its surface in the axial direction [3, 4]. Extruders with a grooved feed section are called *grooved feed extruders*. To avoid excessive pressures that can lead to barrel or screw failure, the length of the grooved barrel section must not exceed 3.5D. A schematic diagram of the grooved section in a single screw extruder is presented in Fig. 4.8. The key factors that propelled the development and refinement of the grooved feed extruder were the processing problems, excessive melt temperature, and reduced productivity posed by high viscosity and low coefficients of friction typical of high molecular weight polyethylenes and polypropylenes.

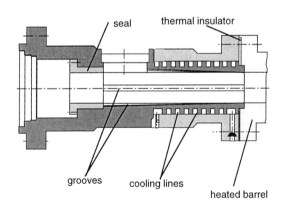

Figure 4.8 Schematic diagram of the grooved feed section of a single screw extruder

In a grooved feed extruder, the conveying and pressure build-up tasks are assigned to the feed section. Figure 4.9 presents the pressure build-up in a single screw extruder with a grooved feed section. The high pressures in the feed section lead to the main advantages over conventional systems. With grooved feed systems, there is a higher productivity and a higher melt flow stability and pressure invariance. This is demonstrated with the screw characteristic curves in Fig. 4.10, which presents screw characteristic curves for a 45 mm diameter grooved feed extruder with comparable mixing sections and die openings as shown in Fig. 4.6.

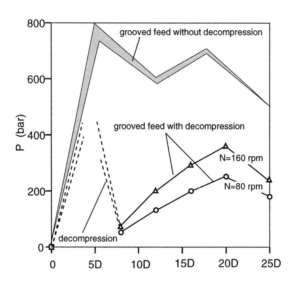

Figure 4.9 Grooved feed extruder pressure distribution

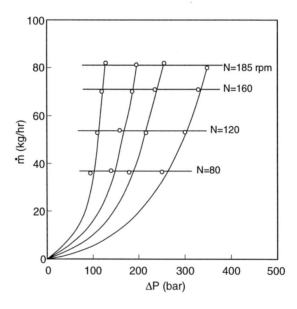

Figure 4.10 Screw and die characteristic curves for a grooved feed 45 mm diameter extruder with an LDPE

The behavior of the two extruders in Figs. 4.6 and 4.10 are best compared if the throughput and the pressure build-up are non-dimensionalized. The dimensionless throughput is

$$\hat{m} = \frac{\dot{m}}{\rho N D^3} \tag{4.2}$$

and the dimensionless pressure build-up is

$$\Delta \hat{p} = \frac{\Delta p D}{m N^n L} \tag{4.3}$$

where L represents the total channel length and for a 25 L/D extruder is

$$L = \frac{25D}{\sin(\phi)} \tag{4.4}$$

where ϕ is assumed to be 17.65° (square pitch). Figure 4.11 presents the results shown in Figs. 4.6 and 4.10 after having been non-dimensionalized using Eqs. (4.2 and 4.3). The figure clearly shows the higher productivity of the grooved feed extruder where the throughput is at least 50% more than that observed with the conventional system for a comparable application. Used with care, Fig. 4.11 can also be used for scale-up.

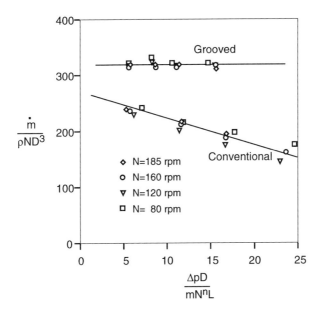

Fig. 4.11 Dimesionless screw charactristic curves for conventional and grooved feed extruders

4.1.2 The Melting Zone

The melting or transition zone is the portion of the extruder were the material melts. The length of this zone is a function of the material properties, screw geometry and processing conditions. During melting, the size of the *solid bed* shrinks as a *melt pool* forms at its side, as depicted in Fig. 4.12a which shows the polymer unwrapped from the screw channel.

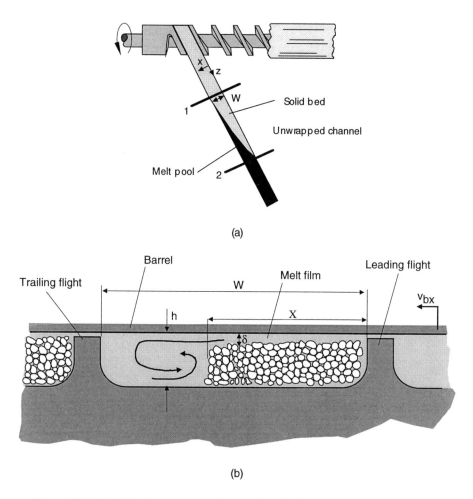

(a)

(b)

Figure 4.12 (a) Solids bed in an unwrapped screw channel and (b) screw channel cross section

Figure 4.12b presents a cross section of the screw channel in the melting zone. The solid bed is pushed against the leading flight of the screw as freshly molten polymer is wiped from the *melt film* into the melt pool by the relative motion between the solids bed and the barrel surface.

Knowing where the melt starts and ends is important when designing a screw for a specific application. The most widely used model to predict melting in a plasticating single screw extruder is the well known Tadmor Model [5]. Using the Tadmor Model, one can accurately predict the solid bed profile in the single screw extruder. Figure 4.13 presents the experimental and predicted solids bed profile of an LDPE in a single screw extruder. The material properties and processing conditions used in the calculations are given in Table 4.2.

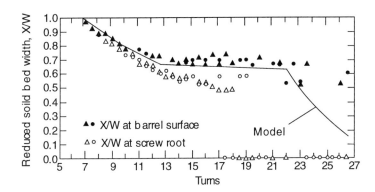

Figure 4.13 Predicted (Tadmor Model) and experimental solids bed profile

Table 4.2 Extruder parameters, processing conditions, and material proprerties for the solids bed profile results in Fig. 4.13

Extruder Geometry:

Square pitch screw, D=63.5mm, L/D=26.5, W=54.16mm
Feed zone   - 12.5 turns h_1=9.4mm
Transition zone - 9.5 turns h_1=9.4mm h_2=3.23mm
Metering zone - 4.5 turns h_2=3.23mm

Processing Conditions:

T_0=24°C T_b=149 °C   N=60 rpm Δp=204 bar $\dot{m}$=61.8 kg/hr

Material properties (LDPE):

Viscosity: n=0.345   a=0.01 °C^{-1} m_0=5.6x10^4 Pa-s^n
T_m=110 °C

Thermal: k_m=0.1817 W/m°C C_m=2.596 kJ/kg°C C_s=2.763 kJ/kg°C
ρ_{bulk}=595 kg/m^3 ρ_s=915.1 kg/m^3 ρ_m=852.7 + 5.018x10^{-7}p - 0.4756T
λ=129.8 kJ/kg

TADMOR'S MELTING MODEL

The Tadmor Model presented in this section was derived using the notation shown in Figs. 4.12a and 4.12b. The non-Newtonian temperature dependent viscosity of the polymer is described by

$$\eta = m_0 e^{-a(T-T_m)} |\dot{\gamma}|^{n-1} \tag{4.5}$$

The solids bed width X in a constant channel depth section is calculated using

$$\frac{X}{W} = \frac{X_0}{W}\left[1 - \frac{\psi(z - z_0)}{2h}\right]^2 \tag{4.6}$$

and in a tapered section with a taper $A = \dfrac{h_1 - h_2}{z_1 - z_2}$ is given as a function of the channel depth

$$\frac{X}{W} = \frac{X_0}{W}\left[\frac{\psi}{A} - \left(\frac{\psi}{A} - 1\right)\sqrt{\frac{h_0}{h}}\right]^2 \tag{4.7}$$

The dimensionless volumetric flow rate ψ is given by

$$\psi = \frac{\Phi}{v_{sz}\rho_{bulk}\sqrt{X_0}} \tag{4.8}$$

where v_{sz} is the velocity of the solid bed in the down-channel direction

$$v_{sz} = \frac{\dot{m}}{\rho_{bulk}Wh} \quad \text{and} \tag{4.9}$$

$$\Phi = \left\{\frac{v_{bx}\rho_m U_2\left[k_m(T_b - T_m) + U_1/2\right]}{2\left[C_s(T_m - T_0) + C_m\overline{\Theta}(T_b - T_m) + \lambda\right]}\right\}^{\frac{1}{2}} \tag{4.10}$$

$$U_2 = 2\left[\frac{1 - b' - e^{-b'}}{b'(e^{-b'} - 1)}\right] \tag{4.11}$$

$$b' = \frac{-a(T_b - T_m)}{n} \tag{4.12}$$

$$U_1 = 2m_0 v_j^{n+1}\delta^{1-n}\frac{(e^{-b'} + b' - 1)}{b'^2}\left(\frac{b'}{1 - e^{-b'}}\right)^{n+1} \tag{4.13}$$

The speed v_j is the relative velocity between the barrel and the solid bed

$$v_j = \sqrt{v_{bx}^2 + (v_{bz} - v_{sz})^2} \tag{4.14}$$

The dimensionless temperature and the film thickness are defined by

$$\overline{\Theta} = \frac{b'/2 + e^{-b'}(1 + 1/b') - 1/b'}{b' + e^{-b'} - 1} \tag{4.15}$$

and

$$\delta = \left\{ \frac{[2k_m(T_b - T_m) + U_1]X}{v_{bx}U_2\rho_m[C_s(T_m - T_{s0}) + C_m\overline{\Theta}(T_b - T_m) + \lambda]} \right\}^{1/2} \tag{4.16}$$

From experiment to experiment there are always large variations in the experimental solids bed profiles. The variations in this section of the extruder are caused by slight variations in processing conditions and by the uncontrolled solids bed break-up towards the end of melting. This effect can be eliminated by introducing a screw with a barrier flight that separates the solids bed from the melt pool. The Maillefer screw and barrier screw in Fig. 4.14 are commonly used for high quality and reproducibility. The Maillefer screw maintains a constant solids bed width, using most effectively the melting with melt-removal mechanism, while the barrier screw uses a constant channel depth with a gradually decreasing solids bed width.

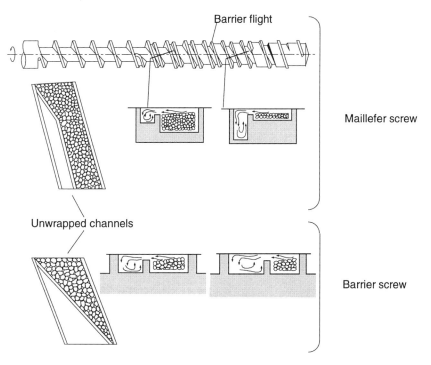

Figure 4.14 Schematic diagram of screws with different barrier flights

4.1.3 The Metering Zone

The metering zone is the most important section in melt extruders and conventional single screw extruders that rely on it to generate pressures sufficient for pumping. The pumping capabilites in the metering section of a single screw extruder can be estimated by solving the equation of motion with appropriate constitutive laws. For a Newtonian fluid in an extruder with a constant channel depth, the screw and die characteristic curves for different cases are represented in Fig. 4.15. The figure shows the influence of the channel depth on the screw characterisctic curves. A restrictive extrusion die would clearly work best with a shallow channel screw, and a less restrictive die would render the highest productivity with a deep channel screw.

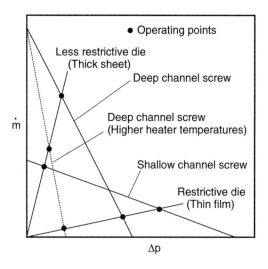

Figure 4.15 Screw characteristic curves (Newtonian)

ANALYTICAL SCREW CHARACTERISTICS CURVES
(NEWTONIAN)

For a Newtonian material, the analytical solution is given by Tadmor [2]. It is

$$Q = \frac{V_{bz}W(h-\delta)}{2}F_d + \frac{Wh^3}{12\eta_0}\left(-\frac{\partial p}{\partial z}\right)F_p(1+f_L) \qquad (4.17)$$

where,

$$V_{bz} = \pi n D cos(\phi) \qquad (4.18)$$

$$tan(\phi) = \frac{L_s}{\pi D} \qquad (4.19)$$

and

$$f_L = \left(\frac{\delta}{h}\right)^3 \frac{e}{W} + \frac{\left(1+\dfrac{e}{W}\right)\left[\dfrac{1+e/W}{tan^2\phi} - \dfrac{6\eta_0 V_{bz}(h-\delta)}{h^3(\partial p/\partial z)}\right]}{1+\left(\dfrac{h}{\delta}\right)^3 \dfrac{e}{W}} \tag{4.20}$$

The shape factors F_d and F_p are necessary to account for the no-slip boundary condition on the channel walls, and can be approximated using functions valid for $(h/W)<0.6$ given by [6]

$$F_d \approx 1 - 0.571\frac{h}{W} \tag{4.21}$$

and

$$F_p \approx 1 - 0.625\frac{h}{W} \tag{4.22}$$

In both the grooved barrel and the conventional extruder, the diameter of the screw determines the metering or pumping capacity of the extruder. Figure 4.16 presents typical normalized mass throughput as a function of screw diameter for both systems.

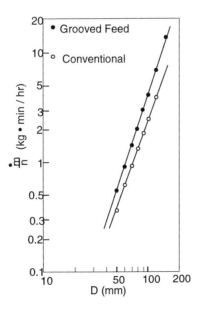

Figure 4.16 Throughput for conventional and grooved feed extruders

4.2 Extrusion Dies

The extrusion die shapes the polymer melt into its final profile. The extrusion die is located at the end of the extruder and it used to extrude:

- Flat films and sheets
- Pipes and tubular films for bags
- Filaments and strands
- Hollow profiles for window frames
- Open profiles

As shown in Fig. 4.17, depending on the functional needs of the product, several rules of thumb can be followed when designing an extruded plastic profile. These are:

- Avoid thick sections. Thick sections add to the material cost and increase sink marks caused by shrinkage.
- Minimize the number of hollow sections. Hollow sections add to die cost and make the die more difficult to clean.
- Generate profiles with constant wall thickness. Constant wall thickness in a profile makes it easier to control the thickness of the final profile and results in a more even crystallinity distribution in semi-crystalline profiles.

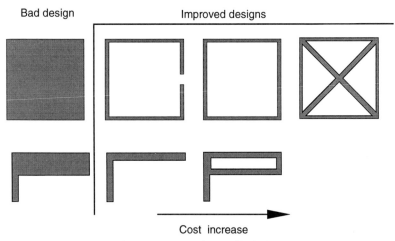

Figure 4.17 Extrusion profile designs

4.2.1 Sheeting Dies

One of the most widely used extrusion dies is the *coat-hanger sheeting die*. A sheeting die, such as depicted in Fig. 4.18 is formed by the following elements:

- Manifold: evenly distributes the melt to the approach or land region
- Approach or land: carries the melt from the manifold to the die lips
- Die lips: perform the final shaping of the melt

• Flex lips: for fine tuning when generating a uniform profile

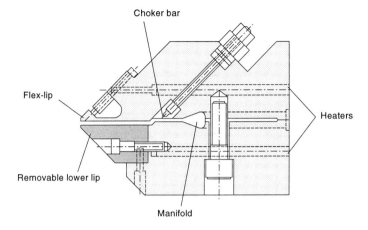

Figure 4.18 Cross section of a coat-hanger die

To generate a uniform extrudate geometry at the die lips, the geometry of the manifold must be specified appropriately. Figure 4.19 presents the schematic of a coat-hanger die with a pressure distribution that corresponds to a die that renders a uniform extrudate. It is important to mention that the flow though the manifold and the approach zone depend on the non-Newtonian properties of the polymer extruded. So the design of the die depends on the shear thinning behavior of polymer. Hence, a die designed for one material does not necessarily work for another.

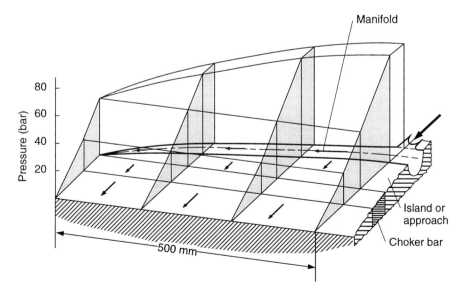

Figure 4.19 Pressure distribution in a coat-hanger die

ANALYTICAL COAT-HANGER DIE

For the isothermal flow of a power-law fluid, using the notation in Fig. 4.20, we can perform a mass balance and solve the equation of motion for the manifold (flow in a tube) and the approach (flow between parallel plates) region. For uniform flow in the die lips, the design equation for a coat-hanger sheeting die is given by [5]

$$R(x) = \left\{ \frac{[(3+s)/\pi]^n h^{2n+1}(W-x)^n}{2^n(s+2)^n \left(\dfrac{dL}{dl}\right)} \right\}^{\frac{1}{3n+1}} \tag{4.23}$$

where $s = 1/n$. For a manifold with a straight axis the manifold curvature can be computed using

$$\frac{dL}{dl} = -\sin\alpha \tag{4.24}$$

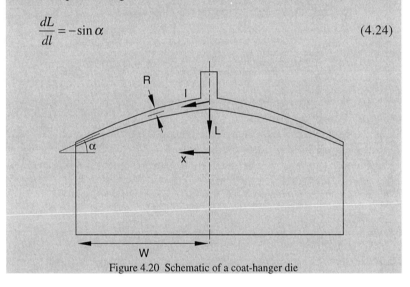

Figure 4.20 Schematic of a coat-hanger die

4.2.2 Tubular Dies

In a tubular die, the polymer melt exits through an annulus. These dies are used to extrude plastic pipes and tubular film. The film blowing operation is discussed in more detail in Chapter 7.

The simplest tubing die is the spider die, depicted in Fig. 4.21. Here, a symmetric mandrel is attached to the body of the die by several legs. The polymer must flow around the spider legs causing weld lines along the pipe or film. These weld lines, visible streaks along the extruded tube, are weaker regions.

To overcome weld line problems, the cross-head tubing die is often used. Here, the die design is similar to that of the coat-hanger die, but wrapped around a cylinder. This die is depicted in Fig. 4.22. Since the polymer melt must flow around the mandrel, the extruded tube exhibits one weld line. In addition, although the eccentricity of a mandrel can be controlled using adjustment screws, there is no flexibility to perform fine tuning such as in the coat-hanger die. This can result in tubes with uneven thickness distributions.

The spiral die, commonly used to extrude tubular blown films, eliminates weld line effects and produces a thermally and geometrically homogeneous extrudate. The polymer melt in a spiral die flows through several feed ports into independent spiral channels wrapped around the circumference of the mandrel. This type of die is schematically depicted in Fig. 4.23.

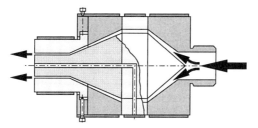

Figure 4.21 Schematic of a spider leg tubing die

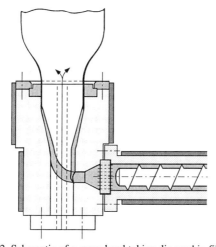

Figure 4.22 Schematic of a cross-head tubing die used in film blowing

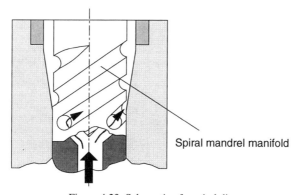

Spiral mandrel manifold

Figure 4.23 Schematic of a spiral die

Examples

4.1 Reproduce the predicted solids bed profile for the solids conveying section in the system found in Fig. 4.13. Use the data presented in Table 4.2.

From the conditions given in Table 4.2, we can first compute the barrel velocity with respect to the screw using

$$v_b = \pi Dn = \pi(0.0635)(1) = 0.1995 \ m/s$$

The down and cross channel velocities are

$$v_{bz} = v_b \cos\phi = (0.1995)\cos(17.65) = 0.1901 \ m/s$$
$$v_{bx} = v_b \sin\phi = (0.1995)\sin(17.65) = 0.0605 \ m/s$$

The velocity of the solids bed is computed using Eq. (4.9)

$$v_{sz} = \frac{(61.8/3600)}{(595)(0.05416)(0.0094)} = 0.0567 \ m/s$$

The relative speed between the solids bed and the barrel is calculated using Eq. (4.14)

$$v_j = \sqrt{(0.0605)^2 + (0.1901 - 0.0567)^2} = 0.1465 \ m/s$$

and using Eqs. (4.12), (4.11), and (4.15), we can compute

$$b' = \frac{-0.01(149-110)}{0.345} = -1.1304$$

$$U_2 = 2\left[\frac{1+1.1304 - e^{1.1304}}{-1.1304(e^{1.1304} - 1)}\right] = 0.8155$$

$$\overline{\Theta} = \frac{-1.1304/2 + e^{1.1304}(1+1/(-1.1304)) - 1/(-1.1304)}{-1.1304 + e^{1.1304} - 1} = 0.7002$$

If we neglect the pressure effects, we can compute the melt density using an average temperature of 129.5 $^{\circ}C$ as

$$\rho_m = 852.7 - 0.4756(129.5) = 791.1 \ kg/m^3$$

Using Eqs. (4.13), (4.16), (4.10), and (4.8), we can compute

$$U_1 = 2(5.6x10^4)(0.1465)^{1.345} \delta^{0.655} \left(\frac{e^{1.1304} - 1.1304 - 1}{(-1.1304)^2}\right)\left(\frac{-1.130}{1 - e^{1.1304}}\right)^{1.1304}$$

$$U_1 = 2786.8\delta^{0.655}$$

$$\delta = \left\{ \frac{[2(0.1817)(149-110)+U_1]X}{(0.0605)(0.8155)(791.1)[2763(110-24)+2596(0.7002)(149-110)+129800]} \right\}^{1/2}$$

$$\delta = 2.418x10^{-4}\left[(14.7+U_1)X\right]^{1/2}$$

$$\Phi = \left\{ \frac{(0.0605)(791.1)(0.8155)[(0.1817)(149-110)+U_1/2]}{2[(2763)(110-24)+(2596)(0.7002)(149-110)+129800]} \right\}^{1/2}$$

$$\Phi = 4.72x10^{-3}\left[14.17+U_1\right]^{1/2}$$

$$\psi = \frac{4.72x10^{-3}\left[14.17+U_1\right]^{1/2}}{(0.0567)(595)\sqrt{0.05416}}$$

$$\psi = 6.01x10^{-4}\left[14.17+U_1\right]^{1/2}$$

Assuming melting begins at the 7th turn,

$$z_0 = \frac{(7-1)(0.0635)}{\sin(17.65)} = 1.26 \ m$$

at which point $X_0 = W$, Eq. (4.6) can be written as

$$\frac{X}{W} = \left[1-53.19\psi(z-1.26)\right]^2$$

U_1, δ, ψ and X must be solved simultaneously from the end of the 6th turn to the middle of the 12th turn. The results are tabulated below.

Turns	z	$\delta \ (m)$	$U_1 \ (N/s)$	ψ	$X \ (m)$	X/W
7.0	1.466	0.0002967	13.63	0.003169	0.05416	1.0000
7.5	1.571	0.0002905	13.44	0.003158	0.05227	0.9651
8.0	1.675	0.0002844	13.26	0.003147	0.05043	0.9311
8.5	1.780	0.0002783	13.07	0.003137	0.04863	0.8979
9.0	1.885	0.0002723	12.88	0.003126	0.04688	0.8656
9.5	1.990	0.0002664	12.70	0.003115	0.04517	0.8340
10.0	2.094	0.0002605	12.52	0.003105	0.04350	0.8032

Turns	z	δ (m)	U_1 (N/s)	ψ	X (m)	X/W
10.5	2.199	0.0002548	12.33	0.003094	0.04188	0.7733
11.0	2.304	0.0002490	12.15	0.003083	0.04030	0.7441
11.5	2.408	0.0002434	11.97	0.003073	0.03876	0.7156
12.0	2.513	0.0002378	11.79	0.003062	0.03726	0.6880
12.5	2.618	0.0002323	11.61	0.003052	0.03580	0.6610

4.2 Draw the screw characteristic curve for a 45 mm diameter melt extruder for a rotational speed of 60 rpm. The extruder has a square pitch, an L/D of 20, a constant channel depth of 2.5 mm, a channel width of 37.88 mm, and a clearance of 0.15 mm. Assume a Newtonian viscosity of 100 Pa-s.

From the above conditions we can first compute the down channel velocity using

$$v_{bz} = \pi Dn\cos\phi = \pi(0.045)(1)\cos(17.65) = 0.1347 \; m/s$$

and the channel length using

$$L = \frac{(L/D)D}{\sin\phi} = \frac{20(0.045)}{\sin(17.65)} = 2.968 \; m$$

Using Eqs. (4.21-22) we can compute the drag and pressure shape factors as

$$F_d \approx 1-0.571\left(\frac{0.0025}{0.045}\right) = 0.968$$

$$F_d \approx 1-0.625\left(\frac{0.0025}{0.045}\right) = 0.965$$

and Eq. (4.20) is used to compute the leakage flow factor as

$$f_L = \left(\frac{0.00015}{0.0025}\right)^3\frac{0.005}{0.03788}+\frac{\left(1+\frac{0.005}{0.03788}\right)\left[1+\frac{1+\frac{0.005}{0.03788}}{\tan^2 17.65}-\frac{6(100)(0.1347)(0.0025-0.00015}{(0.0025)^3(\Delta p/2.968)}\right]}{1+\left(\frac{0.0025}{0.00015}\right)^3\frac{0.005}{0.03788}}$$

$$f_L = 0.0066 - \frac{6.67 x 10^4}{\Delta p}$$

With Eq. (4.17) we can now calculate the flow rate

$$Q = \left[\frac{(0.1347)(0.03788)(0.0025 - 0.00015)}{2}(0.968) - \frac{(0.03788)(0.0025)^3}{12(100)(2.968)}(0.965)\Delta p(1 + f_L) \right]$$

which is converted to kg/h using

$$\dot{m} = Q\rho = Q(1000)(3600)$$

$$\dot{m} = 20.89 - 5.773x10^{-7} \Delta p \left(1.0066 - \frac{6.67x10^4}{\Delta p} \right)$$

The screw characteristic curve without the effect of leakage flow reduces to

$$\dot{m} = 22.23 - 5.773x10^{-7} \Delta p$$

Both curves are plotted in the figure below.

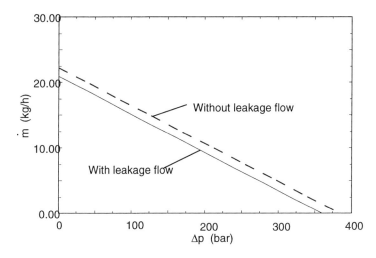

4.3 Formulate a design equation for the end-fed sheeting die shown below such that the extruded sheet is of uniform thickness. Your job is to specify the length of the approach zone or die land as a function of the manifold direction to achieve uniform flow. The manifold diameter is constant and the flow can be assumed isothermal with a Newtonian viscosity of η.

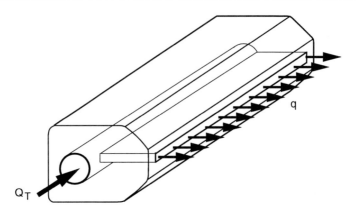

After assigning a coordinate system, and assuming the notation presented in the figure below, the flow of the manifold can be represented using the Hagen-Poiseuille equation as

$$Q = \frac{\pi R^4}{8\eta}\left(-\frac{dp}{dz}\right)$$

and the flow in the die land (per unit width) using slit flow

$$q = \frac{h^3}{12\eta}\left(-\frac{dp}{dl}\right) = \frac{h^3}{12\eta}\left(\frac{p}{L_1}\right)$$

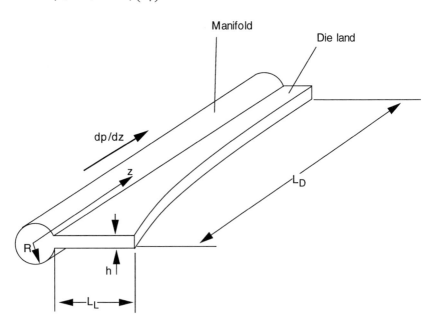

A manifold that leads to a uniform sheet must deliver a constant throughput along the die land. Performing flow balance within the differental element shown below results in

$$Q(z + \Delta z) - Q(z) - q(z)\Delta z = 0$$

and letting $\Delta z \dashrightarrow 0$ results in

$$\frac{dQ}{dz} = -q = \text{constant}$$

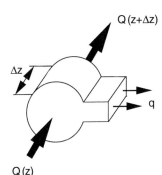

Q (z+Δz)

Δz

q

Q (z)

If we then integrate and let $Q = Q_T$ at $z = 0$ and $Q = 0$ at $z = L_D$ we get

$$Q(z) = Q_T\left(1 - \frac{z}{L_D}\right)$$

Hence,

$$\frac{dQ}{dz} = -\frac{Q_T}{L_D} = -\frac{h^3}{12\eta}\frac{p(z)}{L_l(z)}$$

which results in

$$L_l(z) = \frac{h^3}{12\eta}\frac{L_D}{Q_T}p(z)$$

where $p(z)$ is unknown. We can now rewrite the manifold equation as

$$\frac{dp}{dz} = -\frac{8\eta}{\pi R^4}Q_T\left(1 - \frac{z}{L_D}\right)$$

and then, letting $p = p_0$ at $z = 0$, we get

$$p = p_0 - \frac{8\eta Q_T L_D}{\pi R^4}\left[\left(\frac{z}{L_D}\right) - \frac{1}{2}\left(\frac{z}{L_D}\right)^2\right]$$

which leads to a land length of

$$L_l = \frac{h^3 L_D p_0}{12\eta Q_T} - \frac{2h^3 L_D^2}{3\pi R^4}\left[\left(\frac{z}{L_D}\right) - \frac{1}{2}\left(\frac{z}{L_D}\right)^2\right]$$

Problems

4.1 How would the profile presented in Example 1 be affected by using a more restrictive die which reduces the mass throughput by 20% ?

4.2 Reproduce the predicted solids bed profile for the transition and metering sections in the system presented in Fig. 4.2.

4.3 How would the profile presented in Example 1 be affected if you increase the barrel temperature from 149 to 160 °C ?

4.4 How many turns are required to melt a solids bed for a system similar to the one in Example 1, but using a screw with a constant channel depth of 9.4 mm? How does your result compare to the melting in the three-zoned plasticating extruder?

4.5 You are to extrude a 100 mm wide HDPE sheet using a single screw extruder with 45 mm diameter screw equipped with distributive and dispersive mixing heads. The screw characteristic curve is in the figure below.* The die can be approximated with a 100 mm wide and 100 mm long slit. Typical power-law constants for HDPE at 180 °C are m=20,000 Pa-s^n and n=0.41. Use a specific gravity for HDPE of 0.95.

On the graph below, draw the die characteristic curves for dies with 1 mm and 1.5 mm slits.

Explain the difference between the analytical and the experimental die characteristic curves.

Is it feasible to extrude a sheet through a 1.5 mm slit ? If so, what screw speed would you choose ? What about a 1 mm thick slit ?

---

* Courtesy of ICIPC, Medellín, Colombia.

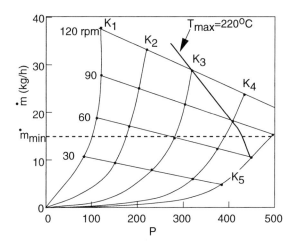

4.6 Plot the screw characteristic curve for the extruder in Example 4.2 once the clearance increases to 0.25 mm as a result of wear.

4.7 Plot the dimensionless screw characteristic curves for the extruder in Example 2 with a clearance of 0, 0.15, and 0.25 mm.

4.8 Plot the dimensionless screw characteristic curves for the extruder of Example 2 with a channel depth of 1.5, 2.5, and 5 mm.

4.9 Formulate the design equation for an end-fed sheeting die such as the one in Example 3. Unlike the example, the new die should have a variable radius manifold as in the figure below. In this case, the axial distance from the manifold center to the die exit must be constant.

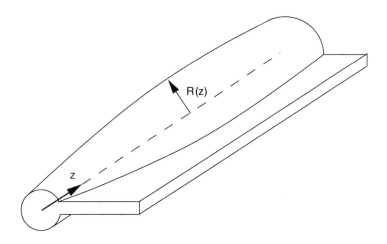

4.10 Formulate the design equation for a coat-hanger die such as shown in Fig.4.20, but with a contant manifold angle α and a Newtonian fluid assumption. Derive an equation for R(x) which results in uniform flow.

4.11 Plot the manifold radius function, Eq. (4.23), for different power law indices, n, a die width of 50 cm, a die thickness of 1 mm and a constant manifold angle of 30°.

4.12 Plot the manifold radius function, Eq. (4.23), for different manifold angles, a die width of 50 cm, a die thickness of 1 mm, and a power-law index of 0.5.

References

1. Darnell, W.H., and E.A.J Mol, *Soc. Plastics Eng. J.* (1956), *12*, 20
2. Tadmor, Z., and I. Klein, *Engineering Principles of Plasticating Extrusion*, Van Nostrand Reinhold Company (1970), New York
3. Menges, G., W. Predöhl, R. Hegele, U. Kosel, and W. Elbe, Plastverarbeiter (1969), (20) 79 and 188
4. Menges, G., U. Kosel, R. Hegele, and W. Elbe, SPE ANTEC (1972), 784
5. Z. Tadmor, and C.G. Gogos, *Principles of Polymer Processing*, John Wiley & Sons (1979), New York
6. Rauwendaal, C., *Polymer Extrusion*, Hanser Publishers (1990), Munich

5 Mixing

The quality of the finished product in almost all polymer processes depends in part how well the material was mixed. Mixing can occur in internal mixers or in processing (e.g., in single and twin screw extruders). Both the material properties and the formability of the compound into shaped parts are highly influenced by the mixing quality. Hence, a better understanding of the mixing process helps one optimize processing conditions and increase part quality.

The process of polymer blending or mixing is accomplished by distributing or dispersing a minor or secondary component within a major component serving as a matrix. The major component can be thought of as the continuous phase, and the minor components as distributed or dispersed phases in the form of droplets, filaments or agglomerates.

When creating a polymer blend, one must always keep in mind that the blend will probably be remelted in subsequent processing or shaping processes. For example, a rapidly cooled system, frozen as a homogenous mixture, can separate into phases because of coalescence when re-heated. For all practical purposes, such a blend is not processable. To avoid this, special macromolecules are commonly used to compatibilize the boundary layers between phases [1].

The mixing can be *distributive* or *dispersive.* The morphology development of polymer blends is determined by three competing mechanisms: distributive mixing, dispersive mixing, and coalescence. Figure 5.1 presents a model, proposed by Macosko and co-workers [1,2], that helps us visualize the mechanisms governing morphology development in polymer blends.

5.1 Distributive Mixing

Distributive mixing or laminar mixing of compatible liquids is usually characterized by the distribution of the droplet or secondary phase within the matrix. This distribution is achieved by imposing large strains on the system such that the interfacial area between phases increases and the local dimensions, or striation thicknesses, of the secondary phases decrease. This concept is shown in Fig. 5.2 [3]. Here we have a Couette flow device with the secondary component having an initial striation thickness of δ_0. As the inner cylinder rotates, the secondary component is distributed through the systems with constantly decreasing striation thickness.

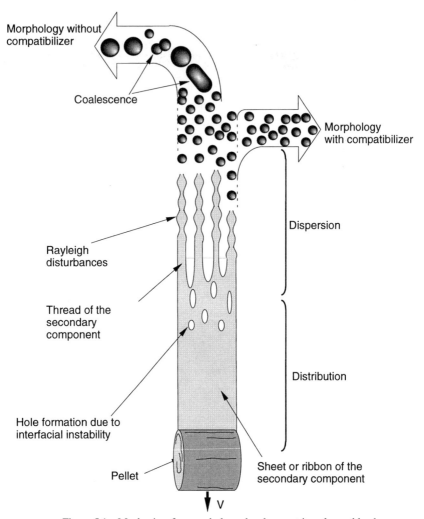

Figure 5.1   Mechanism for morphology development in polymer blends

5.1.1 Effect of Orientation

Imposing large strains on the system may not homogenize the mixture sufficiently. The type of mixing device, initial orientation, and position of the fluid components play a significant role in the quality of mixing. For example, the mixing mechanism shown in Fig. 5.2 homogeneously distributes the melt within the region contained by the streamlines cut across by the initial secondary component. Figure 5.3 [4] shows another variation of initial orientation and arrangement of the secondary component. Here, the secondary phase cuts across all streamlines, which can lead to a homogeneous mixture throughout.

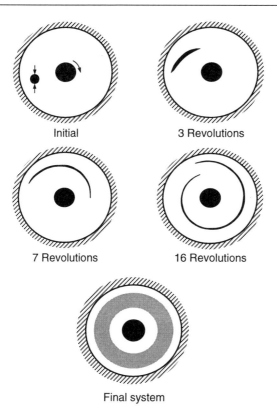

Figure 5.2   Experimental results of distributive mixing in Couette flow, and schematic of the final mixed system

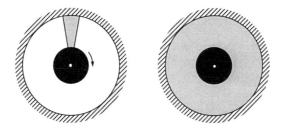

Figure 5.3   Distributive mixing in Couette flow

ESTIMATING DISTRIBUTIVE MIXING

Distributive mixing can be quantified by the reduction in striation thickness. For a sphere deformed into an ellipsoid, the striation thickness can be related to the total strain using

$$\delta = 2R(1 + \gamma^2)^{-1/4}. \tag{5.1}$$

Another common way of quantifying mixing is by following the growth of the interface between the primary and secondary fluids. In simple shear, a simple relation exists between the interfacial area, the strain and the orientation of the area of the secondary fluid with respect to the flow direction [5]:

$$\frac{A}{A_0} = \gamma \cos \alpha \tag{5.2}$$

where A_0 is the initial interfacial area, A is the final interfacial area, γ is the total strain and α the angle between the surface normal vector and the flow direction. Figure 5.4 [6] demonstrates this.

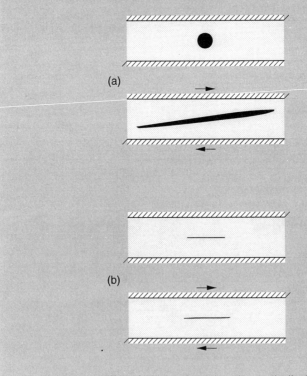

(a)

(b)

Figure 5.4   Effect of initial surface orientation on distributive mixing

Here, both cases (a) and (b) build with equal initial areas, A_0, and undergo the same amount of strain, $\gamma = 10$. The circular secondary component in (a) has a surface that is randomly oriented, between 0 and 2π, whereas most of the surface of the elongated secondary component in case (b) is oriented at $\frac{\pi}{2}$ so that of the interfacial area hardly changes. An ideal case would have been a long slender secondary component with a surface oriented in the flow direction or vertically between the parallel plates. Hence, the maximum interface growth inside a simple shear mixer can be achieved if the direction of the interface is maintained in an optimal orientation ($\cos \alpha = 1$). In a simple shear flow, this would require a special stirring mechanism that would maintain the interface between the primary and secondary fluid components in a vertical position. Using this concept, Erwin [7] demonstrated that the upper bound for the ideal mixer is found in a mixer that applies a plane strain extensional flow or pure shear flow to the fluid. In such a system the growth of the interfacial areas follows the relation given by

$$\frac{A}{A_0} = e^{\gamma/2} \tag{5.3}$$

In Erwin's ideal mixer, the amount of mixing increases exponentially compared to a linear increase if the orientation of the fluids' interfaces remain undisturbed.

5.2 Dispersive Mixing

Dispersive mixing in polymer processing involves breaking a secondary immiscible fluid or an agglomerate of solid particles and dispersing them throughout the matrix. Here, the imposed strain is not as important as the imposed stress which causes the system to break up. Hence, the type of flow inside a mixer plays a significant role in the break up of solid particle clumps or fluid droplets in dispersion.

5.2.1 Break Up of Particulate Agglomerates

The most common example of dispersive mixing of particulate solid agglomerates is the dispersion and mixing of carbon black into a rubber compound. The dispersion of such a system is schematically represented in Fig. 5.5. However, the break-up of particulate agglomerates is best explained using an ideal system of two small spherical particles that must be separated and dispersed during mixing.

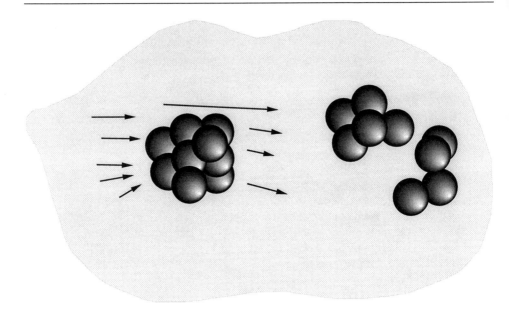

Figure 5.5   Break-up of particulate agglomerates during flow

If the mixing device generates a simple shear flow, as shown in Fig. 5.6, the maximum separation forces on the particles occur when they are oriented in a 45° position as they continuously rotate during flow. The magnitude of the force trying to separate the "agglomerate" is given by [8]

$$F_{shear} = 3 \pi \eta \dot{\gamma} \, r^2 \qquad (5.4)$$

where η is the viscosity of the carrier fluid, $\dot{\gamma}$ the magnitude of the strain rate tensor, and r the radii of the particles.

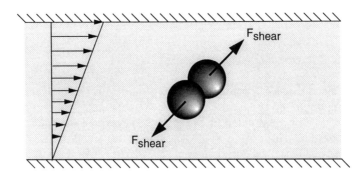

Figure 5.6   Force applied to a two-particle agglomerate in simple shear

However, if the flow field generated by the mixing device is purely elongational, such as shown in Fig. 5.7, the particles always are oriented at 0 °; the position of maximum force. The magnitude of the force for this system is given by

$$F_{elong} = 6 \pi \eta \dot{\gamma} \; r^2 \qquad (5.5)$$

which is twice the maximum tangential force producing simple shear. In addition, in an elongational flow, the agglomerate is always oriented in the direction of maximum force generation, whereas in simple shear flow, the agglomerate tumbles quickly through the position of maximum force.

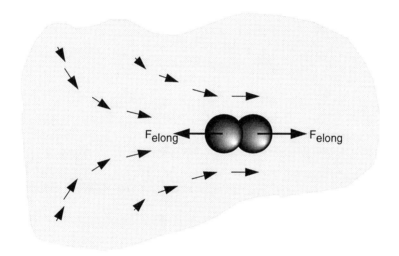

Figure 5.7   Force applied to a two-particle agglomerate in an elongational flow

The above analysis makes it clear that for mixing processes requiring break-up and dispersion of agglomerates, elongation is the preferred mode of deformation. This is only valid if the magnitude of the rate of deformation tensor can be kept the same in elongation as in shear. Hence, when optimizing mixing devices, it is important to know which mode of deformation dominates, which can be accomplished by computing a *flow number* [9], defined by

$$\lambda = \frac{\dot{\gamma}}{\dot{\gamma} + \omega} \qquad (5.6)$$

where $\dot{\gamma}$ is the magnitude of the rate of deformation tensor and ω the magnitude of the vorticity tensor. A flow number of 0 implies pure rotational flow, a value of 0.5 represents simple shear flow, and pure elongational flow is implied when λ equals 1.

5.2.2 Break-Up of Fluid Droplets

Droplets in an incompatible matrix tend to be spherical as a result of their natural tendency to maintain the lowest possible surface to volume ratio. However, a flow field within the mixer applies a stress on the droplets, causing them to deform. If this stress is high enough, it eventually causes the drops to disperse. The droplets disperse when the surface tension can no longer maintain their shape in the flow field and the filaments break up into smaller droplets. This phenomena of dispersion and distribution continues to repeat itself until the stresses of the flow field can no longer overcome the surface tension of the new droplets formed.

As can be seen, the mechanism of fluid agglomerate break-up are similar in nature to solid agglomerate break-up in the sense that both rely on forces to disperse them. Hence, elongation is also the preferred mode of deformation when breaking up fluid droplets and threads, making the flow number, λ, indispensable when quantifying mixing processes.

A parameter commonly used to determine whether a droplet disperses is the capillary number defined by

$$Ca = \frac{\tau \, R}{\sigma_s} \tag{5.7}$$

where τ is the flow induced or deviatoric stress, R the characteristic dimension of the droplet and σ_s the surface tension acting on the drop. The capillary number is the ratio of flow stresses to droplet surface stresses. Droplet break-up occurs when a critical capillary number, Ca_{crit}, is reached. This break-up is clearly shown in Fig. 5.8 [10], which depicts the disintegration of a Newtonian thread in a Newtonian matrix.

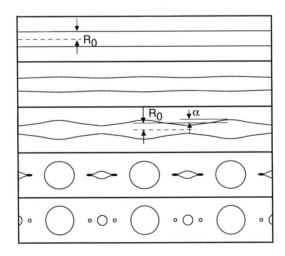

Figure 5.8   Disintegration of a Newtonian 0.35 mm diameter castor oil thread in a Newtonian silicon oil matrix. Redrawn from photographs taken every second

Because of the continuously decreasing thread radius, the critical capillary number is reached at some specific point in time. As a result of the competing deviatoric stresses and surface forces, the cylindrical shape becomes unstable and small disturbances at the surface lead to a growth of capillary waves, commonly called *Rayleigh disturbances.* Disturbances with various wavelengths form on the cylinder surface, but only those with a wavelength exceeding the circumference $(2\pi R_0)$ of the thread lead to a monotonic decrease of the interfacial area.

Figure 5.9 [11] shows the critical capillary number as a function of viscosity ratio, ϕ, and flow type, described by the mixing parameter λ. For a viscosity ratio of 1 the critical capillary number is of order 1 [12]. Distributive mixing is implied when Ca is much greater than Ca_{crit} since the interfacial stress is much smaller than shear stresses. For such a case, the capillary waves which cause droplet break-up would not develop. Dispersive mixing is implied when Ca approaches its critical value or when interfacial stresses nearly equal the deviatoric stresses causing droplet break-up. In addition, break-up can occur only if enough time elapses.

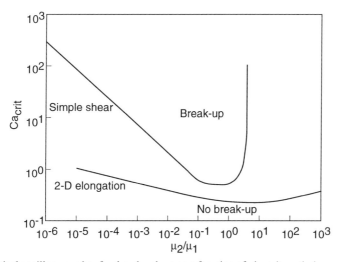

Figure 5.9   Critical capillary number for drop break-up as a function of viscosity ratio in a simple shear and a 2-D elongational flow

BREAK-UP TIME OF INCOMPATIBLE FLUIDS DURING DISPERSION

The time required for break-up, t_b, can be computed using

$$t_b = \frac{5.61}{q} \tag{5.8}$$

where q is given by

$$q = \frac{\sigma_s \Omega}{2\eta_1 R_0} \ . \tag{5.9}$$

and Ω is a dimensionless growth rate represented in Fig. 5.10. The break-up time decreases as the critical capillary number is exceeded. The reduced break-up time t_b^* can be approximated using [11]

$$t_b^* = t_b \left(\frac{Ca}{Ca_{crit}}\right)^{-0.63} . \tag{5.10}$$

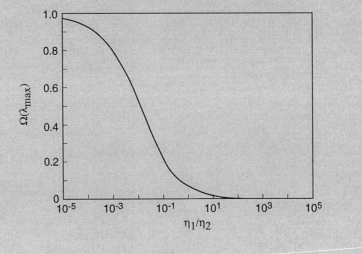

Figure 5.10   Dominant growth rate of interfacial disturbances as a function of viscosity ratio

As mentioned before, surface tension plays a large role in mixing, especially when dealing with dispersive mixing, when the capillary number approaches its critical value. Because of the stretching of the interfacial area caused by distributive mixing, the local radii of the suspended components decrease as surface tension starts to play a role. Once the capillary number goes below its critical value, only slight deformations occur and internal circulation maintains an equilibrium elliptical droplet in the flow. The mixing process then reduces to the distribution of the dispersed droplets.

5.3 Mixing Devices

The final properties of a polymer component are heavily influenced by blending or mixing during processing or as a separate step in the manufacturing process. As mentioned earlier, when measuring the quality of mixing, one must also evaluate the mixing efficiency. For example, the amount of power required to achieve the highest mixing quality for a blend may be unachievable. This section presents mixing devices commonly encountered in polymer processing.

In general, mixers can be classified into two categories: internal batch mixers and continuous mixers. Internal batch mixers, such as the Banbury mixer, are the oldest mixing devices in polymer processing but are slowly being replaced by continuous mixers. This is because most continuous polymer processes involve mixing in addition to their normal processing tasks. Typical examples are single and twin screw extruders that often have mixing heads or kneading blocks incorporated into their systems.

5.3.1 Banbury Mixer

The Banbury mixer, shown in Fig. 5.11, is perhaps the most commonly used internal batch mixer. Internal batch mixers are high intensity mixers that generate complex shearing and elongational flows which work especially well in the dispersion of solid particle agglomerates within polymer matrices. One of the most common applications for high intensity internal batch mixing is the break-up of carbon black agglomerates into rubber compounds. The dispersion of agglomerates depends strongly on mixing time, rotor speed, temperature, and rotor blade geometry [13]. Figure 5.12 [14,15] shows the fraction of undispersed carbon black versus time in a Banbury mixer at 77 rpm and 100 °C. The broken line in the figure represents the fraction of particles smaller than 500 nm.

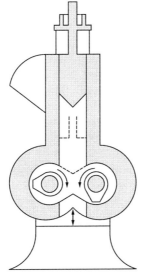

Figure 5.11   Schematic diagram of a Banbury mixer

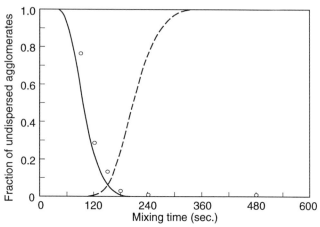

Figure 5.12   Fraction of undispersed carbon black, of size above 9 µm, as a function of mixing time inside a Banbury mixer; (O) denotes experimental results and solid line theoretical predictions; thebroken line denotes the fraction of aggregates below 500 nm in size

5.3.2 Mixing in Single Screw Extruders

One task of a single screw extruder is to mix polymers with additives and to homogenize the melt before pumping it through the die.   As discussed in the previous chapter, even without a mixing section, there is a cross flow component in the polymer melt traveling down the channel in a single screw extruder. This cross flow component acts as a stirring mechanism which causes mixing. By circulating the fluid from the top of the channel to the bottom, and vice versa, the cross-channel component re-orients the interfaces between the primary and secondary fluids, enhancing mixing during extrusion.

Mixing caused by the cross-channel flow component can be further enhanced by introducing pins in the flow channel. These pins can either sit on the screw as shown in Fig. 5.13 [16], or the barrel as shown in Fig. 5.14 [17]. The extruder with the adjustable pins on the barrel is called a QSM-extruder.* In both cases the pins disturb the flow by re-orienting the surfaces between fluids and by creating new surfaces by splitting the flow. The pin type extruder is especially useful for mixing high viscosity materials such as rubber compounds; thus, it is often used in *cold feed rubber extruders*, a machine widely used to produce rubber profiles .

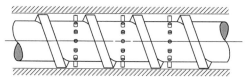

Figure 5.13   Pin mixing section on the screw of a single screw extruder

---

* QSM comes from the German *Quer Strom Misch* which translates as "cross-flow mixing".

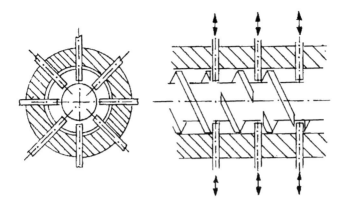

Figure 5.14   Pin barrel extruder

For lower viscosity fluids, such as thermoplastic polymer melts, often the mixing action caused by the cross-flow is insufficient to re-orient, distribute, and disperse the mixture, so one must use special mixing sections. Re-orientation of the interfaces between primary and secondary fluids and distributive mixing can be induced by any disruption in the flow channel. Figure 5.15 [16] presents commonly used distributive mixing heads for single screw extruders. These mixing heads introduce several disruptions in the flow field which improve mixing.

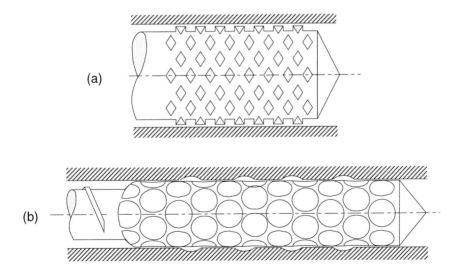

Figure 5.15   Distributive mixing sections: (a) pineapple mixing section, (b) cavity transfer mixing section

As mentioned earlier, dispersive mixing is required when breaking particle agglomerates or when surface tension effects exist between primary and secondary fluids. To disperse such systems, the mixture must be subjected to large stresses. Barrier-type screws are often sufficient to apply high stresses; however, more intensive mixing results from a mixing head. When using barrier screws or a mixing head as shown in Fig. 5.16 [16] the mixture is forced through narrow gaps, causing high stresses in the melt. Most dispersive and distributive mixing heads result in flow resistance, causing viscous heating and pressure losses during extrusion.

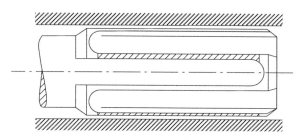

Figure 5.16   Maddock or Union Carbide mixing section

Current dispersive mixing heads have two important drawbacks. One, they rely mostly on shear rather than elongational stresses, and two, the material passes over the high stress region only once. As already discussed earlier, elongational deformation achieves dispersion more effectively than shear, but also, in terms of energy and power consumption, simple shear flows are significantly inferior to any extensional flow.

Recently, a new mixing technology was developed that eliminates these disadvantages of existing single screw extruder mixing heads [17]. The new mixing head has wedged-shaped pushing flights with a large gap, and wedged-shaped slots within the flights, as shown in Fig. 5.17. The wedge shapes generate strong elongational deformations with little viscous dissipation. Experiments performed on PS/HDPE blends show that such a mixing head can break down the dispersed PS phase to an average of 2 μm droplets, with negligible pressure losses and viscous dissipation. The size of the dispersed phase is comparable to co- and counter-rotating twin screw extruders, as discussed in section 5.3.5.

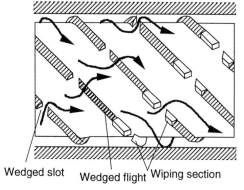

Wedged slot   Wedged flight   Wiping section

Figure 5.17   CRD mixing section.

5.3.3 Static Mixers

Static mixers or motionless mixers are pressure-driven, continuous mixing devices through which the melt is pumped, rotated, and divided, leading to effective mixing without movable parts and mixing heads. One of the most commonly used static mixers is the twisted tape static mixer schematically shown in Fig. 5.18. As the fluid is rotated by the dividing wall, the interfaces between the fluids increase. The interfaces are then re-oriented by 90° once the material enters a new section. The stretching and re-orientation sequence is repeated until the number of striations is so high that a nearly homogeneous mixture is achieved. Figure 5.19 shows a sequence of cuts down a Kenics static mixer.

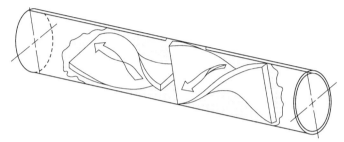

Figure 5.18   Schematic diagram of a Kenics static mixer

The number of striations increase from section to section by 2, 4, 8, 16, 32..., or simply by $N = 2^n$, where N is the number of striations and n the number of sections in the mixer.

Figure 5.19   Experimental progression of the layering of colored resins in a Kenics static mixer. Courtesy of Chemineer, Inc.

Similar to dispersive mixers in single screw extrusion, a major drawback of existing static mixers is that their main mode of deformation is shear rather than elongation. Recently, a new dispersive static mixer was developed that generates elongational deformations, which lead to higher dispersive mixing [18]. Figure 5.20 presents a schematic of the new dispersive static mixer.

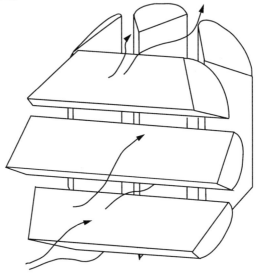

Figure 5.20   Schematic diagram of a disperive static mixer

5.3.4 Cokneader

The cokneader is a single screw extruder with pins on the barrel and a screw that oscillates in the axial direction. Figure 5.21 shows a schematic diagram of a cokneader. The pins on the barrel wipe the entire surface of the screw, making it the only self-cleaning single-screw extruder. This reduces residence time, which makes it appropriate for processing thermally sensitive materials. The pins on the barrel also disrupt the solids bed creating a *dispersed melting* [19], which improves the overall melting rate and reduces the material temperature.

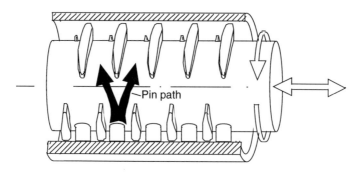

Figure 5.21   Schematic diagram of a cokneader

A simplified analysis of a cokneader gives the following number of striations per L/D [20]

$$N_s = 2^{12} \qquad\qquad (5.11)$$

so that over a section of 4D the number of striations is $2^{12(4)} = 2.8E14$. A detailed discussion on the cokneader is given by Rauwendaal [20] and Elemans [21].

5.3.5 Twin Screw Extruders

In the past two decades, twin screw extruders have developed into the most popular continuous mixing devices. In general, they can be classified into intermeshing or non-intermeshing, and co-rotating or counter-rotating twin screw extruders. The intermeshing twin screw extruders are *self-cleaning* which evens out the polymer residence time. The main characteristic of this configuration is that the screw surfaces slide past each other, constantly removing polymer stuck to the screw.

In the last two decades, the co-rotating twin screw extruder systems have established themselves as efficient continuous mixers for most processes, including reactive extrusion. In essence, the co-rotating systems have a high pumping efficiency caused by the double transport action of the two screws. The counter-rotating systems generate high temperature pulses, making them inappropriate for reactive extrusion, but they generate high stresses because of the calendering action between screws, making them efficient machines to disperse pigments and lubricants.*

Several studies evaluate the mixing capabilities of twin screw extruders. Two recent studies by Lim and White [22, 23] evaluated morphology development in a 30.7 mm screw diameter co-rotating [24] and a 34 mm screw diameter counter-rotating [13] intermeshing twin screw extruder. In both studies, they dry-mixed a 75/25 blend of polyethylene and polyamide 6 pellets and then fed into the hopper at 15 kg/hour. Small samples were taken along the axis of the extruder and evaluated using optical and electron microscopy.

The blend dispersion is manifested by the reduction of the characteristic size of the polyamide 6 phase. Figure 5.22 is a plot of the weight average and number average domain size of the polyamide 6 phase along the screw axis with one kneading-pump element and three special mixing elements.

Using a co-rotating twin screw extruder with three kneading disk blocks, a final morphology with polyamide 6 weight average phase sizes of 2.6 μm was achieved. Figure 5.23 shows the morphology development along the screw axes. When comparing counter-rotating (Fig. 5.22) with co-rotating (Fig. 5.23), both achieve similar final mixing quality. However, the counter-rotating extruder achieved the final morphology much earlier in the screw than the co-rotating twin screw extruder. A possible explanation for this is that the blend traveling through the counter-rotating configuration melted earlier than in the co-rotating geometry. In addition, the phase size was slightly smaller, possibly as a result of the calendering effect between the screws in the counter-rotating system.

---

* There seems to be considerable disagreement about co- versus counter- rotating twin screw extruders between different groups in the polymer processing industry and academic community.

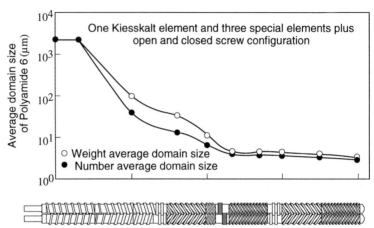

Figure 5.22   Number and weight average of polyamide 6 domain sizes along the screws for a counter-rotating twin screw extruder with special mixing elements

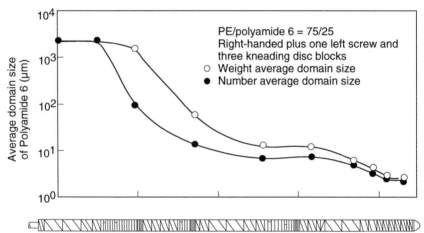

Figure 5.23 Number and weight average of polyamide 6 domain sizes along the screws for a co-rotating twin screw extruder with special mixing elements

Examples

5.1 You are to use a 45 mm diameter single screw extruder to create a polymer polycarbonate/polypropylene polymer blend. The maximum screw rotation is 160 rpm and the screw channel depth is 4mm. Assuming a barrel temperature of 300 °C, a surface tension, σ_s between the two polymers of 8×10^{-3} N/m, and using the viscosity curves given in Figs. 5.24 and 5.25, determine:

• If one can disperse 20% PC into 80% PP
• If one can disperse 20% PP into 80% PC
• The minimum size of the dispersed phase

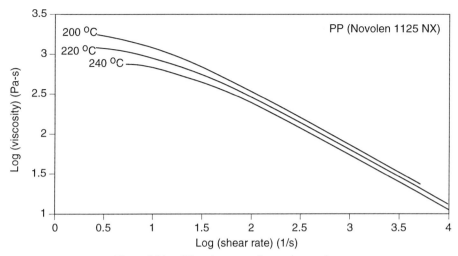

Figure 5.24   Viscosity curves for a polypropylene

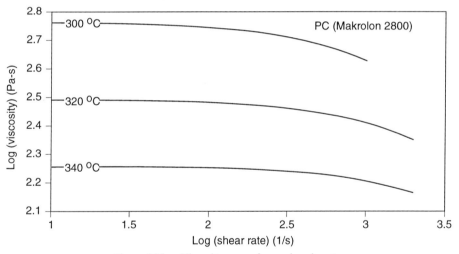

Figure 5.25   Viscosity curves for a polycarbonate

We start this problem by first calculating the average speed in the extruder using

$$v_0 = \pi Dn = \pi(45)(160)(1/60) = 377 \ mm/s$$

which results in an average rate of deformation of

$$\dot{\gamma} = \frac{v_0}{h} = \frac{377}{4} = 94$$

From the viscosity curves we get $\eta_{PC} \approx 600 \ Pa-s \ and \ \eta_{PP} \approx 150 \ Pa-s$.
Using Fig. 5.9 we can deduce that one cannot disperse polycarbonate into

polypropylene using a single screw extruder that only induces shear deformation, since $\eta_{PC}/\eta_{PP} > 4$. On the the other hand, one can disperse polypropylene into polycarbonate using the same single screw extruder.

Using Fig. 5.9 we can see that dispersive mixing for a $\eta_{PC}/\eta_{PP} = 0.25$ will occur at $Ca_{crit} \approx 0.7$. Hence, neglecting the effects of coalescencewe can calculate the minimum size of the dispersed phase using

$$Ca_{crit} = 0.7 = \frac{\tau R}{\sigma_s} = \frac{600(94)R}{8x10^{-3}} \longrightarrow D = 2R = 0.2\,\mu m$$

To achieve this dispersion we must maintain the stresses for an extended period.

Problems

5.1 Estimate the striation thickness of a 3mm diameter pigmented polystyrene pellet in a polystyrene matrix after traveling through a 20 turn, 45 mm diameter, 5 mm constant channel depth, single screw extruder. Assume open discharge conditions. Use 100 rpm rotational speed.

5.2 Someone in your company proposes to use an existing square pitch 150 mm diameter plasticating single screw extruder as a mixing device for a 40/60 PP/PS polymer blend. The metering section is 5 turns long and has a channel depth of 10 mm. Will dispersion of the polypropylene occur for a screw rotation of 60 rpm ? Will there be enough time for dispersion ? Assume open discharge and a temperature of 220 °C. Use viscosity data given in Example 5.1, and in Fig. 5.26.

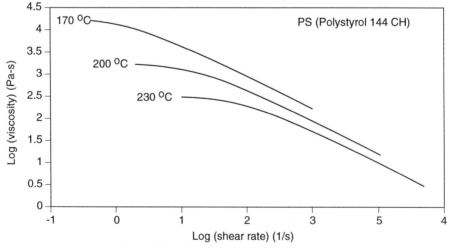

Figure 5.26   Viscosity curves for a polystyrene.

5.3   Someone in your company proposes to use an existing square pitch 150 mm diameter plasticating single screw extruder as a mixing device for a 40/60 PS/PP polymer blend. The metering section is 5 turns long and has a channel depth of 10 mm. Will dispersion of the polystyrene occur for a screw rotation of 60 rpm ? Assume open discharge and a temperature of 220 °C. Use viscosity data given in Figs. 5.24 and 5.26.

5.4   An internal batch mixer maintains shear rates, $\dot{\gamma}$, of 100 s^{-1} for extended periods. In the mixer you want to disperse LDPE in a PS matrix at 170 °C. What is the size of the dispersed phase? Will the PS still be transparent? Use viscosity data given in Figs. 5.26 and 5.27.

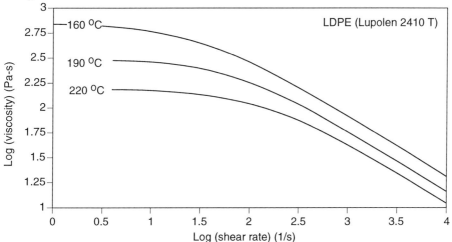

Figure 5.27   Viscosity curves for a low density polyethylene.

References

1.   Sundararaj, U., and C.W. Macosko, *Macromolecules* (1995), *28*, 2647
2.   Scott, C.E., and C.W. Macosko, *Polymer Bulletin* (1991), *26*, 341
3.   Gramann, P.J., L. Stradins, and T.A. Osswald, *Intern. Polymer Processing* (1993), 8, 287
4.   Tadmor, Z., and C.G. Gogos, *Principles of Polymer Processing*, John Wiley & Sons (1979), New, York
5.   Erwin, L., *Polym. Eng. & Sci.* (1978), *18*, 572
6.   Rauwendaal, C., *Mixing in Polymer Processing*, Marcel Dekker, Inc. (1991), New York
7.   Erwin, L., *Polym. Eng. & Sci.* (1978), *18*, 738
8.   Tadmor, Z., *Ind. Eng. Fundam.* (1976), *15*, 346
9   Cheng, J., and I. Manas-Zloczower, *Internat. Polym. Proc.* (1990), 5, 178
10.   Sundararaj, U., and C.W. Macosko, *Macromolecules* (1995), *28*, 2647
11.   Grace, H.P., *Chem. Eng. Commun.* (1982), *14*, 225
12.   Janssen, J.M.H., Ph.D. Thesis (1993), Eindhoven University of Technology, The Netherlands
13.   Biswas, A., and T.A. Osswald (1994), unpublished research
14.   Cox, R.G., *J. Fluid Mech.* (1969), 37, 3, 601–623
15.   Boonstra, B.B., and A.I. Medalia, *Rubber Age* (1963), 3, 4

16. Rauwendaal, C., *Polymer Extrusion*, Hanser Publishers (1990), Munich

17. Rauwendaal, C, T.A. Osswald, P.J. Gramann, and B.A. Davis, *SPE ANTEC Tech. Pap.* (1998), 56

18. Gramann, P..J., B.A. Davis, T.A. Osswald and C. Rauwendaal (1998), Patent Pending

19. Rauwendaal, C., *SPE ANTEC Tech. Pap.* (1993), *39*, 2232

20. Rauwendaal, C., *Mixing in Reciprocating Extruders*, A chapter in *Mixing and Compounding of Polymers*, Eds. I. Manas-Zloczower and Z. Tadmor, Hanser Publishers (1994), Munich

21. Elemans, P.H.M., Modeling of the cokneater, A chapter in *Mixing and Compounding of Polymers*, Eds. I. Manas-Zloczower and Z. Tadmor, Hanser Publishers (1994), Munich

22. Lim, S. and J.L. White, *Intern. Polymer Processing* (1993), *8*, 119

23. Lim, S. and J.L. White, *Intern. Polymer Processing* (1994), *9*, 33

24. Stone, H.A. and L.G. Leal, *J. Fluid Mech.* (1989), 198, 399–427

6 Injection Molding

Injection molding is the most important process used to manufacture plastic products. Today, more than one-third of all thermoplastic materials are injection molded and more than half of all polymer processing equipment is for injection molding. The injection molding process is ideally suited to manufacture mass produced parts of complex shapes requiring precise dimensions. The process goes back to 1872 when the Hyatt brothers patented their stuffing machine to inject cellulose into molds. However, today's injection molding machines are mainly related to the reciprocating screw injection molding machine patented in 1956. A modern injection molding machine with its most important elements is shown in Fig. 6.1. The components of the injection molding machine are the plasticating unit, clamping unit, and the mold.

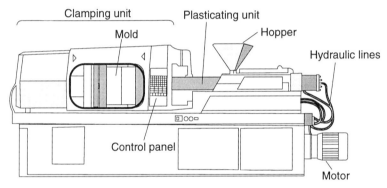

Figure 6.1 Schematic of an injection molding machine

Today, injection molding machines are classified by the following international convention[*]

$$\text{Manufacturer type } T \, / \, P$$

where T is the clamping force in metric tons and P is defined as

$$P = \frac{v_{max} P_{max}}{1000} \tag{6.1}$$

where v_{max} is the maximum shot size in cm^3 and p_{max} is the maximum injection pressure in bar. The clamping forced T can be as low as 1 metric ton for small machines, and as high as 11,000 tons.

[*] The old US convention uses MANUFACTURER T-v where T is the clamping force in British tons and v the shot size in ounces of polystyrene.

6.1 The Injection Molding Cycle

The sequence of events during the injection molding of a plastic part, as shown in Fig. 6.2, is called the injection molding cycle. The cycle begins when the mold closes, followed by the injection of the polymer into the mold cavity. Once the cavity is filled, a holding pressure is maintained to compensate for material shrinkage. In the next step, the screw turns, feeding the next shot to the front of the screw. This causes the screw to retract as the next shot is prepared. Once the part is sufficiently cool, the mold opens and the part is ejected. Fig. 6.3 presents the sequence of events during the injection molding cycle. The figure shows that the cycle time is dominated by the cooling of the part inside the mold cavity. The total cycle time can be calculated using

$$t_{cycle} = t_{closing} + t_{cooling} + t_{ejection}$$ (6.2)

where the closing and ejection times, $t_{closing}$ and $t_{ejection}$, can last from a fraction of second to a few seconds, depending on the size of the mold and machine.

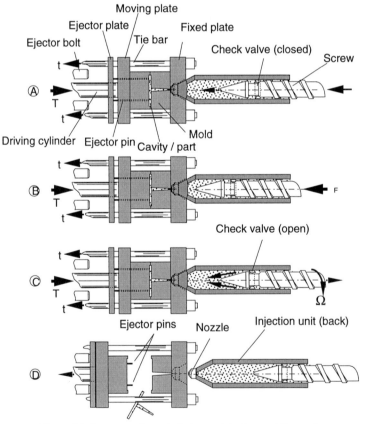

Figure 6.2 Sequence of events during an injection molding cycle

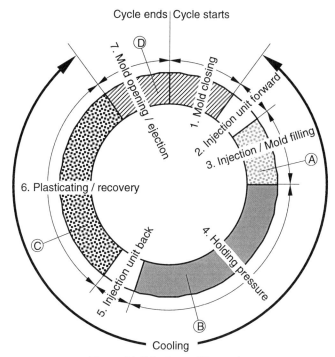

Figure 6.3 Injection molding cycle

ESTIMATING COOLING TIME DURING INJECTION MOLDING

The cooling time for a plate-like part of thickness h can be estimated using [1]

$$t_{cooling} = \frac{h^2}{\pi\alpha}\ln\left(\frac{8}{\pi^2}\frac{T_M - T_W}{T_D - T_W}\right) \tag{6.3}$$

and for cylindrical geometry of diameter D using

$$t_{cooling} = \frac{D^2}{23.14\alpha}\ln\left(0.692\frac{T_M - T_W}{T_D - T_W}\right) \tag{6.4}$$

In Eqs. (6.3) and (6.4), α represents thermal diffusivity, T_M represents the melt temperature, T_W the mold temperature, and T_D the average part temperature at ejection.

Using the average part temperature history and the cavity pressure history, the process can be followed and assessed using the PvT diagram as depicted in Fig. 6.4. [2-3]. To follow the process on the PvT diagram, we must transfer both the temperature and the pressure at matching times. The diagram reveals four basic processes: an isothermal injection (0-1) with pressure rising to the holding pressure (1-2), an isobaric cooling process during the holding cycle (2-3), an isochoric cooling after the gate freezes with a pressure drop to atmospheric (3-4), and then isobaric cooling to room temperature (4-5).

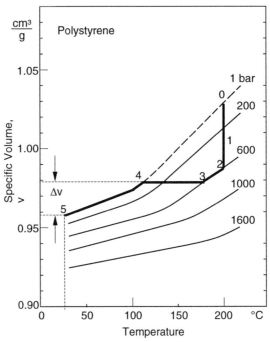

Figure 6.4 Trace of an injection molding cycle in a PvT diagram

The point on the PvT diagram where the final isobaric cooling begins (4), controls the total part shrinkage, Δv. This point is influenced by the two main processing conditions - the melt temperature, T_M and the holding pressure, P_H, as depicted in Fig. 6.5. Here the process in Fig. 6.4 is compared to one with a higher holding pressure. Of course, there is an infinite combination of conditions that render acceptable parts, bound by minimum and maximum temperatures and pressures. Figure 6.6 presents *the molding diagram* with all limiting conditions. The melt temperature is bound by a low temperature that results in a *short shot* or unfilled cavity and a high temperature that leads to material degradation. The hold pressure is bound by a low pressure that leads to excessive shrinkage or low part weight, and a high pressure that results in *flash*. Flash results when the cavity pressure force exceeds the machine clamping force, leading to melt flow across the mold parting line. The holding pressure determines the corresponding clamping force required to size the injection molding machine. An experienced polymer processing engineer can usually determine which injection molding machine is appropriate for a specific application. For the untrained polymer processing engineer, finding this appropriate holding pressure and its corresponding mold clamping force can be difficult.

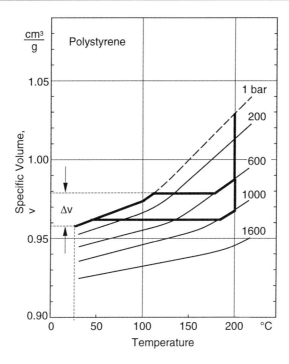

Figure 6.5 Trace of two different injection molding cycles in a PvT diagram

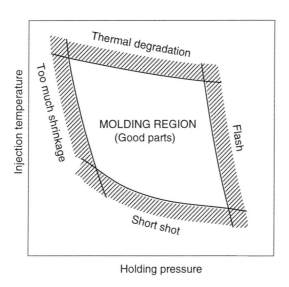

Figure 6.6 The molding diagram

ESTIMATING INJECTION PRESSURE AND CLAMPING FORCE

To aid the polymer processing engineer in finding required injection pressures and corresponding mold clamping forces, Stevenson [4] generated a set of dimensionless groups and corresponding graphs for non-isothermal mold filling of non-Newtonian polymer melts.

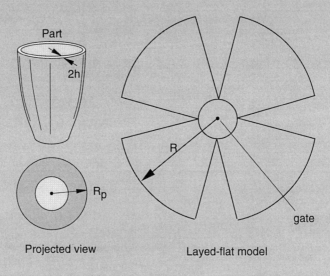

Part

2h

R_p

R

gate

Projected view   Layed-flat model

Fig.6.7 Lay-flat representation of an injection molded part

Using the notation in Fig. 6.7 and a viscosity defined by $\eta = m_0 e^{-a(T-T_{ref})}|\dot{\gamma}|^{n-1}$, four dimensionless groups are defined.

- The dimensionless temperature β determines the intensity of the couplingbetween the energy equation and the momentum balance. It is defined by

$$\beta = a(T_i - T_m) \qquad (6.5)$$

where T_i and T_m are the injection and mold temperatures respectively.

- The dimensionless time τ is the ratio of the filling time, t_{fill}, and the time for thermal equilibrium via conduction, defined by

$$\tau = \frac{t_{fill}k}{h^2 \rho C_p} \qquad (6.6)$$

- The Brinkman number Br is the ratio of the energy generated by viscous dissipation and the energy transported by conduction. For a non-isothermal, non-Newtonian model it is

$$Br = \frac{m_0 e^{-aT_i} h^2}{k(T_i - T_m)} \left(\frac{R}{t_{fill} h} \right)^{n+1}$$

(6.7)

- The power-law index n of the Ostwald and deWaale model reflects the shear thinning behavior of the polymer melt.

Once the dimensionless parameters are calculated, the dimensionless injection pressures $\left(\dfrac{\Delta p}{\Delta p_I} \right)$ and dimensionless clamping forces $\left(\dfrac{F}{F_I} \right)$ are read from Figs. 6.8 to 6.11. The isothermal pressure and force are computed using

$$\Delta p_I = \frac{m_0 e^{-aT_i}}{1-n} \left[\frac{1+2n}{2n} \frac{R}{t_{fill} h} \right]^n \left(\frac{R}{h} \right)$$

(6.8)

and

$$F_I = \pi R^2 \left(\frac{1-n}{3-n} \right) \Delta p_I$$

(6.9)

Since the part area often exceeds the projected area, Fig. 6.12 can be used to correct the computed clamping force.

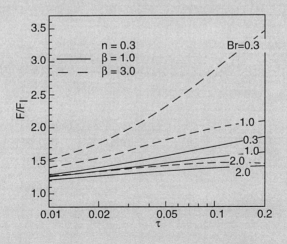

Fig. 6.8 Dimensionless clamping force versus dimensionless groups

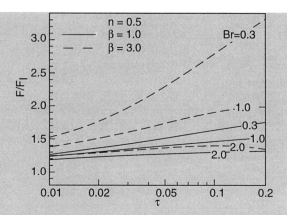

Fig. 6.9 Dimensionless clamping force versus dimensionless groups

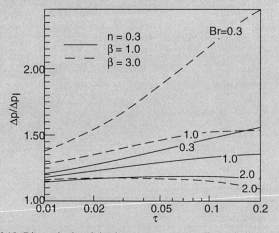

Fig. 6.10 Dimensionless injection pressure versus dimensionless groups

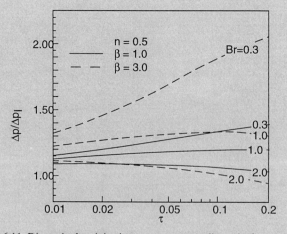

Fig. 6.11 Dimensionless injection pressure versus dimensionless groups

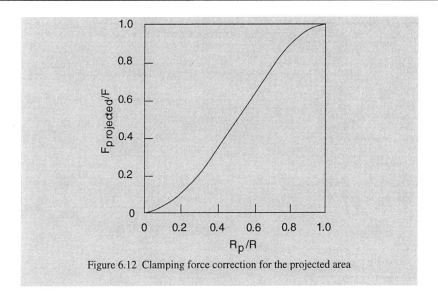

Figure 6.12 Clamping force correction for the projected area

With difficulty, one can control and predict the component's shape and residual stresses at room temperature. For example, *sink marks* in the final product are caused by material shrinkage during cooling, and residual stresses can lead to environmental stress cracking under certain conditions [5].

Warpage in the final product is often caused by processing conditions that lead to asymmetric residual stress distributions through the part thickness. The formation of residual stresses in injection molded parts is attributed to two major coupled factors: cooling and flow stresses. The first and most important is the residual stress formed as a result of rapid cooling.

RESIDUAL STRESSES IN AN INJECTION MOLDED PART

The parabolic temperature distribution through the thickness of a solidified injection molded part leads to a parabolic residual stress distribution, compressive in the outer surfaces of the component and tensile in the core. Assuming no residual stress build-up during phase change, a simple function based on the parabolic temperature distribution, can be used to approximate the residual stress distribution in thin sections [6]:

$$\sigma = \frac{2}{3} \, \alpha \, E \, (\, T_s - T_f \,) \left(\frac{6z^2}{4L^2} - \frac{1}{2} \right) . \qquad (6.10)$$

Here, T_f is the final temperature of the part, E is the modulus, α the thermal expansion coefficient, L the half thickness and T_s denotes the solidification temperature: glass transition temperature for amorphous thermoplastics or the melting temperature for semi-crystalline polymers. Figure 6.13 [7] compares the compressive stresses measured on the surface of PMMA moldings to those predicted by Eq. 6.10.

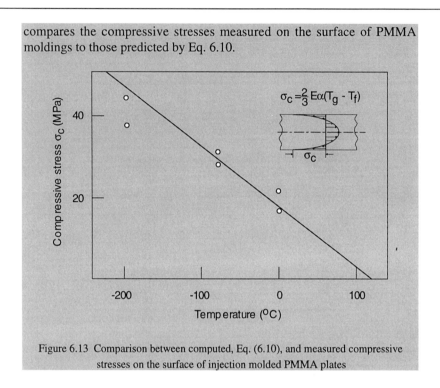

Figure 6.13 Comparison between computed, Eq. (6.10), and measured compressive stresses on the surface of injection molded PMMA plates

6.2 The Injection Molding Machine

6.2.1 The Plasticating and Injection Unit

A plasticating and injection unit is shown in Fig. 6.14. The major tasks of the plasticating unit are to melt the polymer, to accumulate the melt in the screw chamber, to inject the melt into the cavity, and to maintain the holding pressure during cooling.

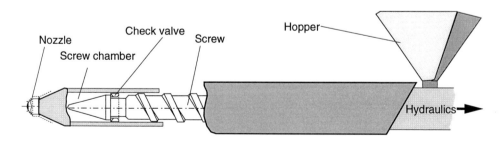

Figure 6.14. Schematic of the plasticating unit

The main elements of the plasticating unit follow:

- Hopper
- Screw
- Heater bands
- Check valve
- Nozzle

The hopper, heating bands and the screw are similar to a plasticating single screw extruder, except that the screw in an injection molding machine can slide back and forth to allow for melt accumulation and injection. This characteristic gives it the name *reciprocating screw*. The maximum stroke in a reciprocating screw is 3D.

Although the most common screw used in injection molding machines is the three-zone plasticating screw, two stage vented screws are often used to extract moisture and monomer gases just after the melting stage.

The check valve, or non-return valve, is at the end of the screw and enables it to work as a plunger during injection and packing without allowing polymer melt back flow into the screw channel. A check valve and its function during operation is depicted in Fig. 6.2, and in Fig. 6.14. A high quality check valve allows less then 5% of the melt back into the screw channel during injection and packing.

The nozzle is at the end of the plasticating unit and fits tightly against the sprue bushing during injection. The nozzle type is either open or shut-off. The open nozzle is the simplest, rendering the lowest pressure consumption.

6.2.2 The Clamping Unit

The job of a clamping unit in an injection molding machine are to open and close the mold, and to close the mold tightly to avoid flash during the filling and holding. Modern injection molding machines have two predominant clamping types: mechanical and hydraulic.

Figure 6.15 presents a toggle mechanism in the open and closed mold positions. Although the toggle is essentially a mechanical device, it is actuated by a hydraulic cylinder. The advantage of using a toggle mechanism is that as the mold approaches closure the available closing force increases and the closing decelerates significantly. However, the toggle mechanism only transmits its maximum closing force when the system is fully extended.

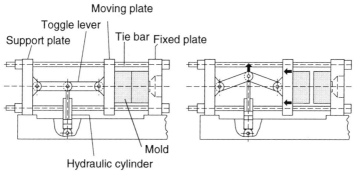

Figure 6.15. Clamping unit with a toggle mechanism

Figure 6.16 presents a schematic of a hydraulic clamping unit in the open and closed positions. The advantages of the hydraulic system is that a maximum clamping force is attained at any mold closing position and that the system can take different mold sizes without major system adjustments.

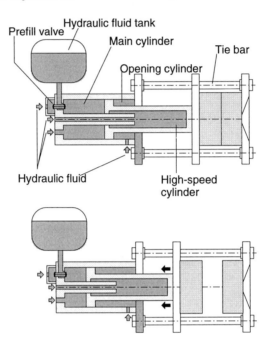

Figure 6.16 Hydraulic clamping unit

6.2.3 The Mold Cavity

The central point in an injection molding machine is the mold. The mold distributes polymer melt into and throughout the cavities, shapes the part, cools the melt and ejects the finished product. As depicted in Fig. 6.17, the mold is custom-made and consists of the following elements:

- Sprue and runner system
- Gate
- Mold cavity
- Cooling system (thermoplastics)
- Ejector system

During mold filling, the melt flows through the sprue and is distributed into the cavities by the runners, as in Fig. 6.18.

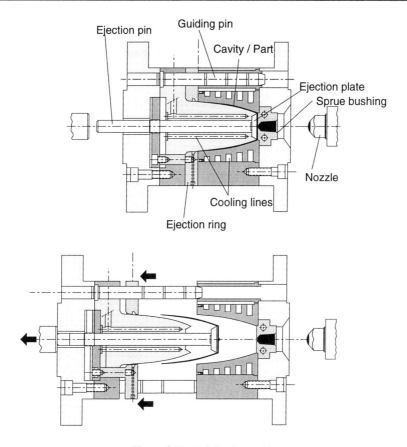

Figure 6.17 An injection mold

The runner system in Fig. 6.18 (a) is symmetric where all cavities fill at the same time causing the polymer to fill all cavities in the same way. The disadvantage of this balanced runner system is that the flow paths are long, leading to high material and pressure consumption. On the other hand, the asymmetric runner system shown in Fig. 6.18(b) leads to parts of different quality. Equal filling of the mold cavities can also be achieved by varying runner diameters. There are two types of runner systems - cold and hot. Cold runners are ejected with the part, and are trimmed after mold removal. The advantage of the cold runner is lower mold cost. The hot runner keeps the polymer at its melt temperature. The material stays in the runners system after ejection, and is injected into the cavity in the following cycle. There are two types of hot runner system: externally and internally heated. The externally heated runners have a heating element surrounding the runner that keeps the polymer isothermal. The internally heated runners have a heating element running along the center of the runner, maintaining a polymer melt that is warmer at its center and possibly solidified along the outer runner surface. Although a hot runner system considerably increases mold cost, its advantages include elimination of trim and lower pressures for injection.

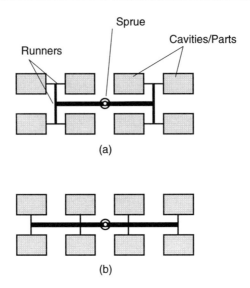

Figure 6.18 Schematic of different runner system arrangements

When large items are injection molded, the sprue sometimes serves as the gate, as shown in Fig. 6.19. The sprue must be subsequently trimmed, often requiring further surface finishing. On the other hand, a pin-type gate (Fig. 6.19) is a small orifice that connects the sprue or the runners to the mold cavity. The part is easily broken off from such a gate, leaving only a small mark that usually does not require finishing. Other types of gates, also shown in Fig. 6.19, are film gates, used to eliminate orientation and disk or diaphragm gates for symmetric parts such as compact discs.

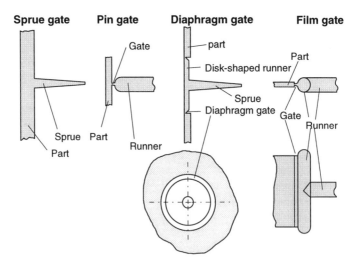

Figure 6.19 Schematic of different gating systems

6.3 Related Injection Molding Processes

Although most injection molding processes are covered by the conventional process description discussed earlier in this chapter, there are several important molding variations including:

- Multi-color
- Multi-component
- Co-injection
- Gas-assisted
- Injection-compression

Multi-color injection molding occurs when two or more components are injected through different runner and gate systems at different stages during the molding process. Each component is injected using its own plasticating unit. The molds are often located on a turntable. Multi-color automotive stop lights are molded this way.

In principle, the multi-component injection molding process is the same as the multi-color process. Here, either two incompatible materials are molded or one component is cooled sufficiently so that the two components do not adhere to each other. For example, to mold a ball and socket system, the socket of the linkage is molded first. The socket component is allowed to cool somewhat and the ball part is injected inside it. This results in a perfectly movable system. This type of injection molding process is used to replace tedious assembling tasks and is becoming popular in countries where labor costs are high.

In contrast to multi-color and multi-component injection molding, co-injection molding uses the same gate and runner system. Here, the component that ends as the outer skin of the part is injected first, followed by the core component. The core component displaces the first and a combination of the no-slip condition between polymer and mold and the freezing of the melt creates a sandwiched structure as depicted in Fig. 6.20.

In principle, the gas-assisted injection molding process is similar to two-component injection molding. Here, the second or core component is nitrogen, which is injected through a needle into the polymer melt, blowing the melt out of the way and depositing it against the mold surfaces.

Injection-compression molding first injects the material into a partially opened mold, and then squeezes the material by closing the mold. Injection-compression molding is used for polymer products that require a high quality surface finish, such as compact discs and other optically demanding components.

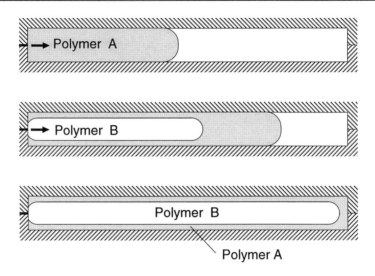

Figure 6.20 Schematic of the co-injection molding process

6.4 Computer Simulation in Injection Molding

Today, computer simulation is commonly used to predict mold filling, fiber orientation, thermal history, residual stresses and warpage in complex parts. It is common practice, to determine gate location, balance the runner system, relocate or eliminate possible weldlines, reduce shrinkage and warpage, and optimize the properties of the finished product before ever cutting a piece of metal, through the use of simulation packages.

In injection molding, researchers are making progress on solving three-dimensional orientation for complex realistic applications [8,9]. Commercially available programs solve for the non-isothermal, non-Newtonian filling and orientation in non-planar injection molded parts. They used the Hele–Shaw model [10] to simulate the mold filling. For example, Fig. 6.21 presents the filling pattern and weldline location during molding of a complex lawn-mover housing. Orientation in the finished product is computed using tensor representations. The injection molded part is divided into layers to include complex flow and heat transfer phenomena that take place during filling. Figure 6.22 presents the fixed finite element mesh used to represent a plate and the predicted filling pattern during molding. The same figure presents the computed fiber orientation distribution in three different layers within the part.

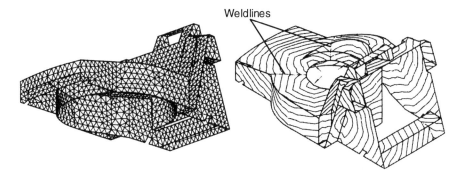

Figure 6.21   Finite element mesh and predicted filling pattern for a lawn-mover housing

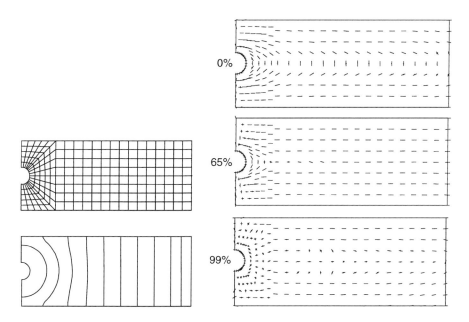

Figure 6.22   Finite element mesh, predicted filling pattern and computed fiber orientation in three
different layers (0% corresponds to the center and 100% to the surface of the part)

Examples

6.1 Consider the multi-cavity injection molding process shown in Fig. 6.23. To achieve
equal part quality, the filling time for all cavities must be balanced. For the case in
question, balance your cavities by solving for the runner radius, R_2. For a balanced
runner system the flow rates into all cavities must match. For a given flow rate Q,
length L, and radius R_1, you must also solve for the pressures at the runner system
junctures. Assume an isothermal flow of a Newtonian polymer with viscosity η.

Compute the radius R_2 for a part molded of polycarbonate with a viscosity of 350 Pa-s. Use values of $L=10$ cm, $R_1=4$ mm, and $Q = 20$ cm/s.

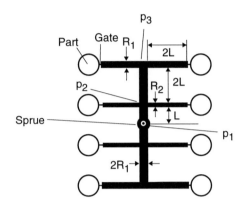

Figure 6.23 Runner system lay out

The flow through each runner section is governed by the Hagen-Poiseuille equation:

$$Q = \frac{\pi R^4}{8\eta}\left(-\frac{dp}{dz}\right)$$

The various sections can be represented using

Section 1: $4Q = \dfrac{\pi(2R_1)^4}{8\eta}(P_1 - P_2)$

Section 2: $2Q = \dfrac{\pi(2R_1)^4}{8\eta}(P_2 - P_3)$

Section 3: $Q = \dfrac{\pi(R_2)^4}{8\eta}(P_2 - 0)$

Section 4: $Q = \dfrac{\pi(R_1)^4}{8\eta}(P_3 - 0)$

The unknown parameters, P_1, P_2, P_3, and R_2, can be obtained using the above equations. For the given values, a radius, R_2, of 3.78 mm would result in a balanced runner system, with pressures $P_1 = 104.4$ bar, $P_2 = 87.0$ bar and $P_3 = 69.6$ bar.

6.2 You are to determine the maximum clamping force and injection pressure required to mold an ABS suitcase with a filling time, t_f, of 2.5 seconds. Use the dimensions shown in Fig. 6.24, an injection temperature, T_i, of 227 °C (500K), and a mold temperature, T_m, of 27 °C (300K). The properties necessary for the calculations are also given below.

Properties for ABS

$n = 0.29$	$\rho = 1020 \ kg/m^3$
$m_0 = 29x10^6 \ Pa-s^n$	$C_p = 2343 \ J/kg/K$
$a = 0.01369/K$	$k = 0.184 \ W/m/K$

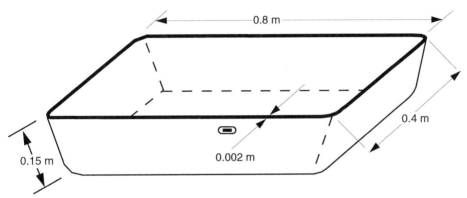

Figure 6.24 Suitcase geometry

We start this problem by first laying the suitcase flat and determining the required geometric factors (Fig. 6.25). From the suitcase geometry, the longest flow path, R, is 0.6 m and the radius of the projected area, R_p, is 0.32 m. We can now compute the dimensionless parameters given in Eqs. (6.5 to 6.7),

$$\beta = 0.01369(500 - 300) = 2.74$$

$$\tau = \frac{2.5(0.184)}{(0.001)^2(1020)(2343)} = 0.192$$

$$Br = \frac{(29x10^6)e^{-0.01369(500)}(0.001)^2}{0.184(500 - 300)} \left(\frac{0.6}{2.5(0.001)}\right)^{0.29+1} = 0.987$$

The isothermal injection pressure and clamping force are computed using Eqs. (6.8 to 6.9)

$$\Delta p_I = \frac{29x10^6 e^{-0.01369(500)}}{1 - 0.29} \left[\frac{1 + 2(0.29)}{2(0.29)} \frac{0.6}{2.5(0.001)}\right]^{0.29} \left(\frac{0.6}{0.001}\right) = 171 \ MPa$$

$$F_l = \pi(0.6)^2 \left(\frac{1-0.29}{3-0.29}\right)(17.1x10^7) = 50.7x10^6 \ N$$

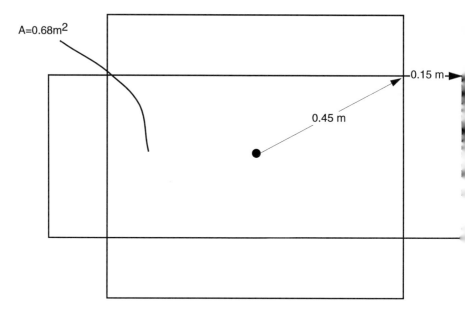

A=0.68m²

0.15 m

0.45 m

Figure 6.25 Layed-flat suitcase

We now look up $\frac{\Delta p}{\Delta p_I}$ and $\frac{F}{F_I}$ in Figs. (6.8 to 6.11). Since little change occurs between n = 0.3 and n = 0.5, we choose n = 0.3. However, for other values of n we can interpolate or extrapolate. For $\beta = 2.74$, we interpolate between 1 and 3 as

$$\beta = 1 \rightarrow \frac{\Delta p}{\Delta p_I} = 1.36 \text{ and } \frac{F}{F_I} = 1.65$$

$$\beta = 3 \rightarrow \frac{\Delta p}{\Delta p_I} = 1.55 \text{ and } \frac{F}{F_I} = 2.1$$

$$\beta = 2.74 \rightarrow \frac{\Delta p}{\Delta p_I} = 1.53 \text{ and } \frac{F}{F_I} = 2.04$$

$$\Delta p = \left(\frac{\Delta p}{\Delta p_I}\right)\Delta p_I = 262 \ MPa = 2,620 \ bar$$

$$F = \left(\frac{F}{F_I}\right)F_I = 10.3x10^7 \ N = 10,300 \ metric \ tons$$

The clamping force can be corrected for an $R_p = 0.32\ m$ using Fig. 6.12 and $R_p/R = 0.53$.

$$F_{projected} = (0.52)10,300 = 5,356\ metric\ tons$$

For our suitcase cover, where the total volume is 1,360 cc and total part area is 0.68 m², the above numbers are too high. A usefull rule-of-thumb is a maximum allowable clamping force of 2 tons/in². Here, we have greatly exceeded that number. Normally, around 3,000 metric tons/m² are allowed in commercial injection molding machines. For example, a typical injection molding machine* with a shot size of 2,000 cc has a maximum clamping force of 630 metric tons with a maximum injection pressure of 1,400 bar. A machine with much larger clamping forces and injection pressures is suitable for much larger parts. For example, a machine with a shot size of 19,000 cc allows a maximum clamping force of 6,000 metric tons with a maximum injection pressure of 1,700 bar. For this example we must reduce the pressure and clamping force requirements. This can be accomplished by increasing the injection and mold temperatures or by reducing the filling time. Recommended injection temperatures for ABS are between 210 and 240 °C and recommended mold temperatures are between 40 and 90 °C.** As can be seen, there is room for adjustment in the processing conditions, so one must repeat the above procedure using new conditions.

Problems

6.1 A thin polyamide 66 component is injection molded under the following conditions:

- The melt is injected at 275 °C to a maximum pack/hold pressure of 800 bar.
- The 800 bar pack/hold pressure is maintained until the gate freezes off, at which point the part is at an average temperature of 175 °C.
- The pressure drops to 1 bar as the part cools inside the cavity.
- The part is removed from the mold and cooled to 25 °C.

• Draw the whole process on the PvT diagram.

• Estimate the final part thickness if the mold thickness is 1 mm. For thin injection molded parts, most of the shrinkage leads to part thickness reduction.

---

* MINIFLOW, Injection Molding Simulation, The Madison Group: PPRC, Madison, WI.
** A good reference for such values is the CAMPUS® material data bank. Books such as H. Domininghaus, *Plastics for Engineers*, Hanser Publishers (1992), Munich are also recommended.

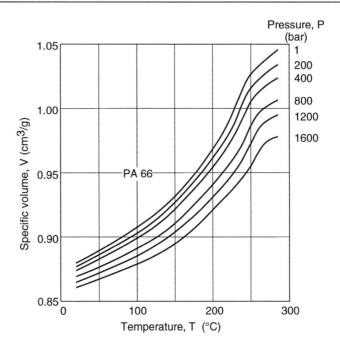

Figure 6.26 PvT diagram for PA66

6.2 Design a balanced runner system for the mold in Example 1 if you are to injection mold a polystyrene product. Assume a power-law model with a consistency index, m, of 2.8×10^4 Pa-s^n, and a power-law index, n, of 0.28.

6.3 Estimate the cooling time for the ABS suitcase presented in Example 6.2 if demolding occurs when the average part temperature is below 60 °C.

6.4 What are the required clamping force and injection pressure if the filling time in Example 6.2 is increased from 2.5 seconds to 3 seconds?

6.5 What are the required clamping force and injection pressure if the mold temperature in Example 6.2 is increased from 27°C to 90°C ?

6.6 What are the required clamping force and injection pressure if the injection temperature in Example 6.2 is increased from 227 to 240 °C?

6.7 What is the residual stress on the surface of a 1 mm thick injection molded polystyrene ruler with a glass transition temperature of 100 °C and a mold temperature of 40 °C? Assume a modulus of 3.2 GPa.

References

1. Pötsch, G., and W. Michaeli, Injection Molding: An Introduction, Hanser Publishers (1995), Munich
2. Greener, J., *Polym. Eng. Sci.* (1986), *26*, 886
3. Michaeli, W., and M. Lauterbach, *Kunststoffe* (1989), *79*, 852
4. Stevenson, J.F., *Polym. Eng. Sci.*((1978), *18*, 577
5. Osswald, T.A., and G. Menges, *Materials Science of Polymers for Engineers,* Hanser Publishers (1996), Munich
6. Wimberger-Friedl, R., *Polym. Eng. Sci.* (1990), *30*, 813
7. Ehrenstein, G.W., *Polymer Kunststoffe,* Hanser Publishers (1978), Munich
8. Verleye, V., and F. Dupret, *Proc. ASME WAM* (1993), New Orleans
9. Crochet, M.J., F. Dupret, and V. Verleye, *Flow and Rheology in Polymer Composites Manufacturing*, Ed. S.G. Advani, Elsevier (1994), Amsterdam
10. Hele-Shaw, H.S., *Proc. Roy. Inst.* (1899), *16*, 49

7 Secondary Shaping

Secondary shaping operations such as extrusion blow molding, film blowing, and fiber spinning occur immediately after the extrusion profile emerges from the die. The thermoforming process is performed on sheets or plates previously extruded and solidified. In general, secondary shaping operations consist of mechanical stretching or forming of a preformed cylinder, sheet, or membrane.

7.1 Fiber Spinning

Fiber spinning is used to manufacture synthetic fibers. During fiber spinning, a filament is continuously extruded through an orifice and stretched to diameters of 100 µm and smaller. The process is schematically depicted in Fig. 7.1. The molten polymer is first extruded through a filter or *screen pack*, to eliminate small contaminants. The melt is then extruded through a spinneret, a die composed of multiple orifices. A spinneret can have between one and 10,000 holes. The fibers are then drawn to their final diameter, solidified, and wound onto a spool. The solidification takes place either in a water bath or by forced convection. When the fiber solidifies in a water bath, the extrudate undergoes an adiabatic stretch before cooling begins in the bath. The forced convection cooling, which is more commonly used, leads to a non-isothermal spinning process.

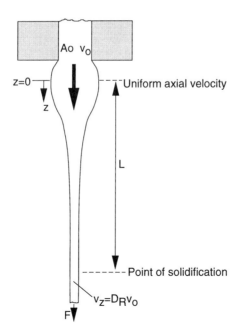

Figure 7.1 The fiber spinning process

The drawing and cooling processes determine the morphology and mechanical properties of the final fiber. For example, ultra high molecular weight HDPE fibers with high degrees of orientation in the axial direction can have the stiffness of steel with today's fiber spinning technology.

Of major concern during fiber spinning are the instabilities that arise during drawing, such as brittle fracture, Rayleigh disturbances, and draw resonance. Brittle fracture occurs when the elongational stress exceeds the melt strength of the drawn polymer melt. The instabilities caused by Rayleigh disturbances are like those causing filament break-up during dispersive mixing as discussed in Chapter 5. Draw resonance appears under certain conditions and manifests itself as periodic fluctuations that result in diameter oscillation.

STABILITY ANALYSIS OF FIBER SPINNING

Fisher and Denn [1] performed a stability analysis of isothermal, viscoelastic spinning. Figure 7.2 [1] presents the stable and unstable regions in a draw ratio, D_R, versus $De^{1/n}$ graph. The draw ratio is defined by

$$D_R = \frac{v_0}{v_f} \tag{7.1}$$

and for this case the Deborah number is given by

$$De = \frac{m(3)^{(n-1)/2}}{G}\left(\frac{v_0}{L}\right) \tag{7.2}$$

where n is the power-law index, m the consistency index, G the shear modulus of the fiber, v_0 the material speed as it emerges from the spinneret orifice, v_f the fiber speed at the take-up roll and, L the distance between the spinneret and the first contact take-up wheel.

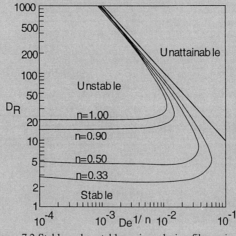

Figure 7.2 Stable and unstable regions during fiber spinning

7.2 Film Production

7.2.1 Cast Film Extrusion

In a cast film extrusion process, a thin film is extruded through a slit onto a chilled, highly polished, turning roll where it is quenched from one side. The speed of the roller controls the draw ratio and final film thickness. The film is then sent to a second roller for cooling of the other side. Finally, the film passes through a system of rollers and is wound onto a roll. A typical film casting process is depicted in Fig. 7.3. The cast film extrusion process exhibits stability problems similar to those encountered in fiber spinning [2].

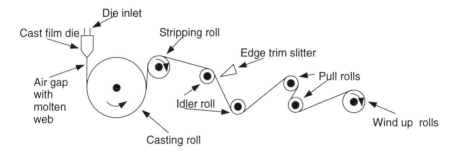

Figure 7.3 Schematic of a film casting operation

Thicker polymer sheets are manufactured similarly. A sheet is distinguished from a film by its thickness; by definition a sheet has a thickness exceeding 250 μm; otherwise, it is called a film.

STABILITY ANALYSIS OF FILM CASTING

Anturkar and Co [2] performed a stability analysis of isothermal, viscoelastic film casting depicted in Fig. 7.4. In their analysis, they used the White-Metzner viscoelastic model and represented the viscosity with the Bird-Carreau model as

$$\eta = \eta_0 \left(1 + \lambda_v^2 \dot{\gamma}^2\right)^{n-\frac{1}{2}}$$
(7.3)

If we relate the time constant of the White-Metzner model to first normal stress differences and viscosity using $\lambda = \dfrac{\psi_1}{2\eta}$, we end with a similar relation for the relaxation time:

$$\lambda = \lambda_0 \left(1 + \lambda_t^2 \dot{\gamma}^2\right)^{n-\frac{1}{2}}$$
(7.4)

Figures 7.5 and 7.6[2] present the stable and unstable regions in a draw ratio, D_R, versus De graph. Here, the Deborah number is defined by

$$De = \frac{\lambda_0 v_0}{L}\left(2\frac{\lambda_t v_0}{L}\right)^{n'-1} \tag{7.5}$$

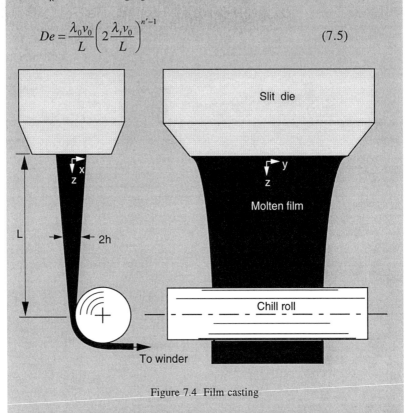

Figure 7.4 Film casting

The curves in Figs. 7.5 and 7.6 show the effect of the exponent n and n', respectively.

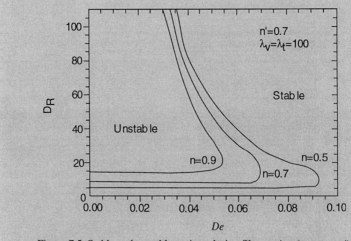

Figure 7.5 Stable and unstable regions during film casting (constant n')

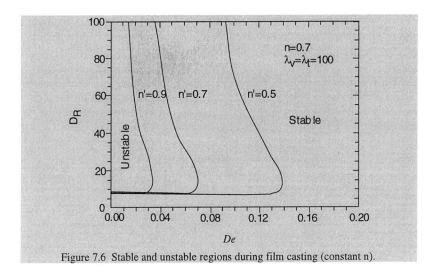

Figure 7.6 Stable and unstable regions during film casting (constant n).

7.2.2 Film Blowing

In film blowing, a tubular cross-section is extruded through an annular die, normally a spiral die, and is drawn and inflated until the *freezing line* is reached. Beyond this point, the stretching is practically negligible. The process is schematically depicted in Fig. 7.5 [3]. The advantage of film blowing over casting is that the induced biaxial stretching renders a stronger and less permeable film.

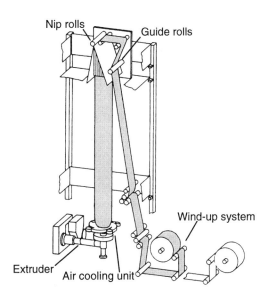

Figure 7.5 Film blowing

The extruded tubular profile passes through one or two air rings to cool the material. The tube interior is maintained at a certain pressure by blowing air into the tube through a small orifice on the die mandrel. The air is retained in the tubular film, or bubble, by collapsing the film well above its freeze-off point and tightly pinching it between rollers. The size of the tubular film is calibrated between the air ring and the collapsing rolls.

FILM BLOWING ANALYSIS

The important outcome of a film blowing process (Fig. 7.6) is the size or diameter of the tubular film defined by the dimensionless blow-up ratio

$$B_R = \frac{R_f}{R_0} \tag{7.6}$$

and the dimensionless draw ratio

$$D_R = \frac{v_f}{v_0} \tag{7.7}$$

Conservation of mass leads to a dimensionless thickness defined by

$$\frac{h_0}{h_f} = B_R D_R \tag{7.8}$$

Pearson and Petrie [4] developed and solved a Newtonian model of film blowing and plotted their results in dimensionless graphs. In addition to dimensionless blow-up ratio, draw ratio, and thickness, they introduced a dimensionless pressure, P,

$$P = \frac{\pi R_0^3 \Delta p}{\mu Q} \tag{7.9}$$

a dimensionless take-up force, F,

$$F = \frac{R_0 f_z}{\mu Q} \tag{7.10}$$

and a dimensionless freeze-off point, X,

$$X = \frac{Z}{R_0} \tag{7.11}$$

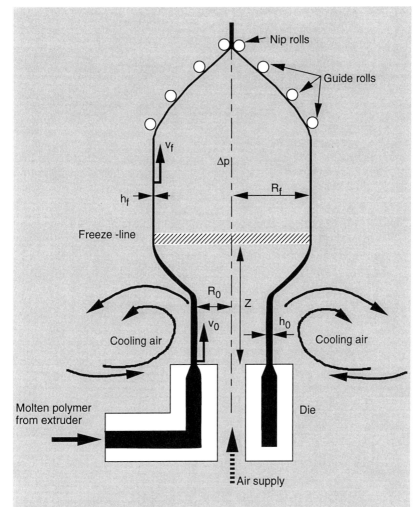

Figure 7.6 Film blowing

where μ is the Newtonian viscosity, R_0 is the radius of the extruded tube, R_f is the radius of the final tubular film, v_0 is the velocity of the material at the exit of the die, v_f is the take-up speed, Q is the volumetric material throughput, Δp is the pressure difference across the film, and f_z is the film take-up force. Figures 7.7[4] and 7.8[4] present results from the isothermal Newtonian film blowing calculations using the above dimensionless parameters. These graphs are helpful when determining effect of processing conditions on film size and thickness.

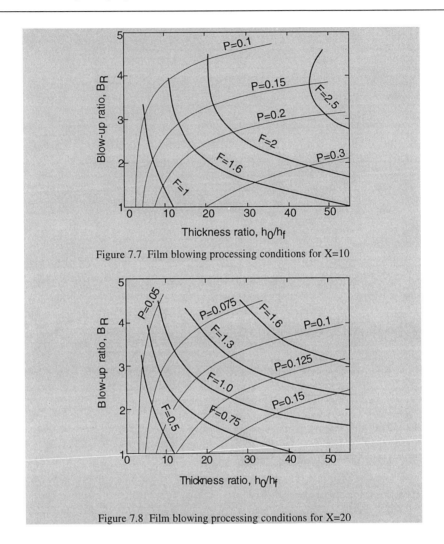

Figure 7.7 Film blowing processing conditions for X=10

Figure 7.8 Film blowing processing conditions for X=20

7.3 Blow Molding

The predecessor of the blow molding process was the blowing press develop by Hyatt and Burroughs in the 1860s to manufacture hollow celluloid articles. Polystyrene was the first synthetic polymer used for blow molding during World War II and polyethylene was the first material to be implemented in commercial applications. Until the late 1950s, the main application for blow molding was the manufacture of LDPE articles such as squeeze bottles.

Blow molding produces nearly hollow articles that do not require a homogeneous thickness distribution. Today, HDPE, LDPE, PP, PET, and PVC are the most common materials used for blow molding.

7.3.1 Extrusion Blow Molding

In extrusion blow molding, a *parison* or tubular profile is extruded and inflated into a cavity with the specified geometry. The blown article is held inside the cavity until it is sufficiently cool. Figure 7.9 [5] presents a schematic of the steps in blow molding.

During blow molding, one must generate the appropriate parison length such that the trim material is minimized. Another means of saving material is by generating a parison of variable thickness, usually referred to as *parison programming*, such that an article with an evenly distributed wall thickness is achieved after stretching the material. An example of a programmed parison and finished bottle thickness distribution is presented in Fig. 7.10 [6].

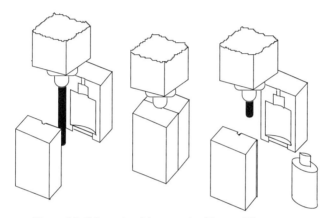

Figure 7.9 Schematic of the extrusion blow molding process

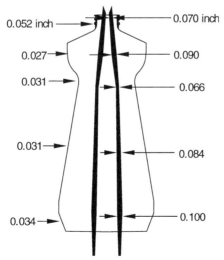

Figure 7.10 Wall thickness distribution in the parison and the part

A parison of variable thickness can be generated by moving the mandrel vertically during extrusion as shown in Fig. 7.11. A thinner wall not only results in material savings but also reduces the cycle time due to the shorter required cooling times.

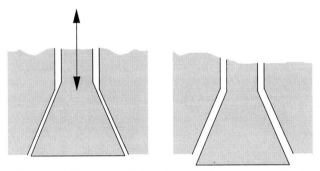

Figure 7.11 Moving mandrel used to generate a programmed parison

As expected, the largest portion of the cycle time is the cooling of the blow molded container in the mold cavity. For this reason, for high volume applications, rotary molds are often used in conjunction with vertical or horizontal rotating tables (Fig. 7.12 [5]).

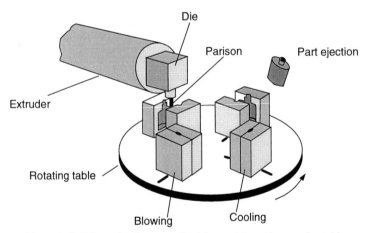

Figure 7.12 Schematic of an extrusion blow molder with a rotating table

COOLING TIME FOR BLOW MOLDING

The same procedure used for injection molding can be used to estimate the cooling time during blow molding. Since the article is cooled from one side only, the inner surface can be considered insulated. The modified Eq. (6.3) now becomes

$$t_{cooling} = \frac{4h^2}{\pi\alpha}\ln\left(\frac{8}{\pi^2}\frac{T_m - T_w}{T_D - T_w}\right) \tag{7.12}$$

7.3.2 Injection Blow Molding

Injection blow molding depicted in Fig. 7.13 [5], begins by injection molding the parison onto a core and into a mold with finished bottle threads. The formed parison has a thickness distribution that leads to reduced thickness variations throughout the container. Before blowing the parison into the cavity, it can be mechanically stretched to orient molecules axially, Fig. 7.14 [5]. The subsequent blowing operation introduces tangential orientation. A container with biaxial molecular orientation exhibits higher optical (clarity) and mechanical properties and lower permeability. In the injection blow molding process one can go directly from injection to blowing or one can have a re-heating stage in-between.

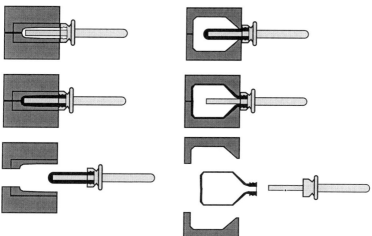

Figure 7.13 Injection blow molding

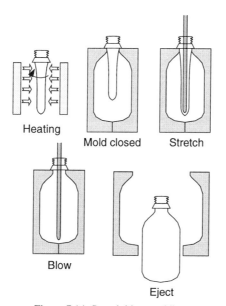

Heating   Mold closed   Stretch

Blow

Eject

Figure 7.14 Stretch blow molding

The advantages of injection blow molding over extrusion blow molding are:

- Pinch-off and therefore post-mold trimming are eliminated
- Controlled container wall thickness
- Dimensional control of the neck and screw-top of bottles and containers

Disadvantages include higher initial mold cost and the need for both injection and blow molding units.

7.4 Thermoforming

Thermoforming is an important secondary shaping of plastic film and sheet. Thermoforming consists of warming the plastic sheet and forming it into a cavity or over a tool using vacuum, air pressure, and mechanical means. During the 18th century, tortoiseshells and hooves were thermoformed into combs and other shapes. The process was refined during the mid-19th century to thermoform various cellulose nitrate articles. During World War II, thermoforming was used to manufacture acrylic aircraft cockpit enclosures, canopies, and windshields, as well as translucent covers for outdoor neon signs. During the 1950s, the process made an impact in the mass production of cups, blister packs, and other packaging commodities. Today, in addition to packaging, thermoforming is used to manufacture refrigerator liners, pick-up truck cargo box liners, shower stalls, bathtubs, as well as automotive trunk liners, glove compartments, and door panels.

A typical thermoforming process is presented in Fig. 7.15 [3]. The process begins by heating the plastic sheet slightly above the glass transition temperature, for amorphous polymers, or slightly below the melting point, for semi-crystalline materials. Although, both amorphous and semi-crystalline polymers are used for thermoforming, the process is easiest with amorphous polymers because they have a wide rubbery temperature range above the glass the transition temperature. At these temperatures the polymer is easily shaped, but still has enough rigidity to hold the heated sheet without much sagging. Most semi-crystalline polymers lose their strength rapidly once the crystalline structure breaks up above the melting temperature.

The heating is achieved using radiative heaters and the temperature reached during heating must be high enough for sheet shaping, but low enough so the sheets do not droop into the heaters. One key requirement for successful thermoforming is to bring the sheet to a uniform forming temperature. The sheet is then shaped into the cavity over the tool. This can be accomplished in several ways. Most commonly a vacuum sucks the sheet onto the tool, stretching the sheet until it contacts the tool surface. The main problem here is the irregular thickness distribution that arises throughout the part. Hence, the main concern of the process engineer is to optimize the system such that the differences in thickness throughout the part are minimized. This can be accomplished many ways but most commonly by plug-assist. Here, as the plug pushes the sheet into the cavity, only the parts of the sheet not touching the plug-assist stretch. Since the unstretched portions of the sheet must remain hot for subsequent stretching, the plug-assist is made of a low thermal conductivity material such as wood or hard rubber. The initial stretch is followed by a vacuum for final shaping. Once cooled, the product is removed.

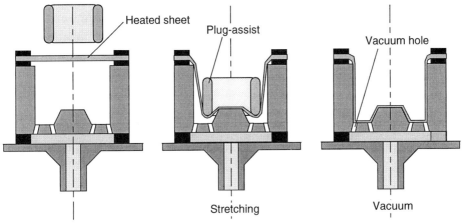

Figure 7.15 Plug-assist thermoforming using vacuum

To reduce thickness variations in the product, the sheet can be prestretched by forming a bubble at the beginning of the process. This is schematically depicted in Fig. 7.16 [3]. The mold is raised into the bubble, or a plug-assist pushes the bubble into the cavity, and a vacuum finishes the process.

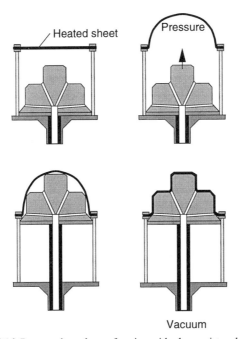

Figure 7.16 Reverse draw thermoforming with plug-assist and vacuum

One of the main reasons for the rapid growth and high volume of thermoformed products is that the tooling costs for a thermoforming mold are much lower than for injection molding.

ANALYSIS OF THERMOFORMING

The thickness distribution in various thermoformed shapes can be predicted using a simple volume or mass balance. For a thermoformed conical shape, shown in Fig. 7.17, the final thickness distribution is given by

$$h = h_0 \frac{1 + \cos \alpha}{2} \left[1 - \frac{s}{H} \sin \alpha \right]^{\sec \alpha - 1} \tag{7.13}$$

This equation can also be used to estimate the thickness distribution in a truncated cone or cup. The thickness distribution in the cylindrical shape shown in Fig. 7.18 is given by

$$h = \frac{h_0}{2} e^{-\frac{s}{R}} \tag{7.14}$$

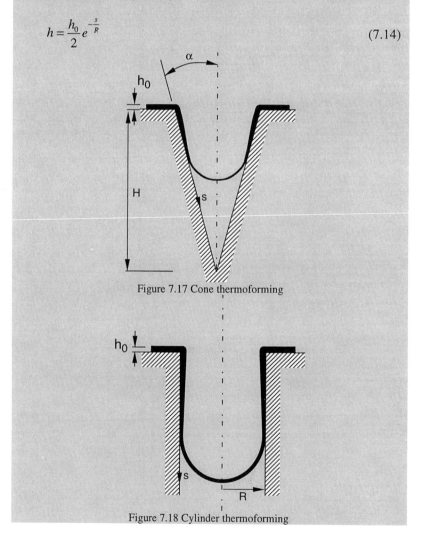

Figure 7.17 Cone thermoforming

Figure 7.18 Cylinder thermoforming

Examples

7.1 Polyethylene fibers are spun to a draw ratio, D_R, of 10 through 500 μm diameter orifices at mass flow rates, $\dot{m}$, of 0.18 kg/hr per fiber. For the data below, will draw resonance occur for a spinning length of 2 m ?

Material data: $n = 0.5$, $m = 2000\ Pa - s^n$, $G = 3000\ Pa$, and $\rho = 960\ kg/m^3$.

To solve this problem, we must first compute the speed of the polyethylene as it emerges from the spinneret

$$v_0 = \dot{m}/(A\rho) = \frac{0.18}{(60)(60)\pi(0.00025)^2(960)} = 0.265\ m/s$$

We can now compute the Deborah number using Eq. (7.2)

$$De = \frac{2000(3)^{(n-1)/2}}{3000}\left(\frac{0.265}{2}\right) = 0.067$$

This gives $De^{1/n} = 0.0045$ which lies in the unstable regime in Fig. 7.2. For a draw ratio of 10 and n = 0.5, the stable regime of $De^{1/n}$ lies between 0.035 and 0.1. To eliminate draw resonance, the distance between the spinneret and the take-up wheel must be decreased to 0.72 m, which requires faster cooling.

7.2 An LLDPE film is blown to a thickness of 50 μm from a 25 mm diameter annular die with a 1 mm thick slit. Determine the required bubble pressure and take-up force for an extruder mass throughput of 100 kg/hr and draw-down ratio, D_R, of 4. The freezing point is 200 mm above the die exit; the polymer is assumed to be Newtonian with a viscosity of 1000 Pa-s; and the density is 920 kg/m³. What is the take-up speed?

We start the solution by calculating the dimensionless freezing point, X, and the thickness ratio, h_0/h_f, as

$$X = \frac{200}{12.5} = 16$$

$$h_0/h_f = \frac{0.001}{50x10^{-6}} = 20$$

From Eq. (7.8), we can compute the blow-up ratio as

$$B_R = \frac{h_0/h_f}{D_R} = \frac{20}{4} = 5$$

Figures 7.7 and 7.8 represent the film blowing process for dimensionless freezing points of 10 and 20, respectively. We can get P and F from the figures and iterpolate for a dimensionless freezing point of 16:

$X = 10 \rightarrow P = 0.08$ and $F = 1.95$

$X = 20 \rightarrow P = 0.055$ and $F = 1.50$

$X = 16 \rightarrow P = 0.065$ and $F = 1.68$

Using Eqs. (7.9) and (7.10), we can now solve for the bubble pressure and the take-up force as:

$$\Delta p = \frac{0.065(1000)(100)(1/60)(1/60)(1/920)}{\pi(0.0125)^3} = 319 \ Pa$$

$$f_z = \frac{1.68(1000)(100)(1/60)(1/60)(1/920)}{(0.0125)} = 4.06 \ N$$

The take-up speed can be computed using

$$v_f = \frac{(100)(1/60)(1/60)(1/920)}{(50x10^{-6})(0.025)(5)\pi} = 1.54 \ m/s$$

7.3 Derive Eq. (7.14) which describes the thickness distribution in a long cylindrical thermoformed container.

The first step in the drawing process is the formation of a spherical bubble of thickness h_1. Through conservation of mass we can equate

$$\pi R^2 h_0 = 2\pi R^2 h_1$$

which results in $h_1 = \frac{h_0}{2}$. At any time, the bubble thickness as it travels down the cylinder is h. As the contact point in Fig. 7.18 travels from S to $S + dS$, it deposits a cylindrical strip of thickness h and width dh on the cylinder wall. A mass balance would result in

$$2\pi R^2 h = 2\pi R^2 (h + dh) + 2\pi Rhds$$

which reduces to

$$\frac{dh}{h} = -\frac{ds}{R}$$

which can be integrated with a boundary condition $h = h_1$ at $s = 0$ to give

$$h = \frac{h_0}{2} e^{-\frac{s}{R}}$$

Problems

7.1 Polyethylene fibers are spun to a draw ratio, D_R, of 20 through 300 μm diameter orifices at mass flow rates, $\dot{m}$, of 0.10 kg/hr per fiber. Using the data in Example 7.1, find the range of allowable distances between the spinneret and the take-up wheel.

7.2 A polyethylene film is cast as shown in Fig. 7.4 at a speed of 0.3 m/s with a draw ratio of 10. Use Figs. 3.2 and 3.7 to determine the constants in Eqs. (7.3) and (7.4).

7.3 In Example 7.2, a faster cooling rate results in a freezing point of 130 mm above the die. What is the new bubble pressure requirement?

7.4 What is the bubble pressure required for the process presented in Example 7.2, but with a blow-up ratio requirement of 4? What is the take-up speed?

7.5 What is the cooling time required for a 0.5 mm thick HDPE blow molded bottle. The extrudate temperature is 150 $^{\circ}$C, and the mold temperature is 40 $^{\circ}$C. The bottle can be safely removed from the cavity when the average temperature is 60 $^{\circ}$C. Material data: $\rho = 950 \ kg/m^3$, $C_p = 2300 \ J/kg/K$ and $k = 0.63 \ W/m/K$

7.6 Derive Eq. (7.13) which describes the thickness distribution in a thermoformed conical container.

7.7 Plot the thickness distribution along the wall of a 100 mm diameter, 400 mm deep cylindrical container thermoformed out of a polystyrene sheet initially 2 mm thick.

7.8 Plot the thickness distribution along the wall of a thermoformed 100 mm deep polystyrene juice cup. The cup mouth and bottom are 70 and 40 mm in diameter, respectively. The sheet was initially 1 mm thick.

References

1. Fisher, R.J., and M.M. Denn, *AIChE J.* (1976), 22, 236
2. Anturkar, N.R., and A. Co, *J. Non-Newtonian Fluid Mech.* (1988), *28*, 287
3. Menges, G., *Einführung in die Kunststoffverarbeitung*, Hanser Publishers (1986), Munich
4. Pearson, J.R.A., and C.J.S. Petrie, *Plastics & Polymers* (1970), *38*, 85
5. Rosato, D.V, and D.V. Rosato, *Blow Molding Handbook*, Hanser Publishers (1989), Munich
6. Modern Plastics Encyclopedia, 53, McGraw-Hill (1976), New York

8 Other Important Polymer Processes

8.1 Calendering

In a calender line, the polymer melt is transformed into films and sheets by squeezing it between pairs of co-rotating high precision rollers. Calenders are also used to produce certain surface textures which may be required for different applications. Today, calendering lines are used to manufacture PVC sheet, floor covering, rubber sheet, and rubber tires. They are also used to texture or emboss surfaces. When producing PVC sheet and film, calender lines have a great advantage over extrusion processes because of the shorter residence times, resulting in a lower requirement for stabilizer. This can be cost effective since stabilizers are a major part of the overall expense of processing these polymers.

Figure 8.1 [1] presents a typical calender line for manufacturing PVC sheet. A typical system is composed of:

- Plasticating unit
- Calender
- Cooling unit
- Accumulator
- Wind-up station

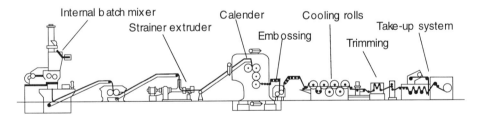

Figure 8.1 Schematic of a typical calendering process (Berstorff GmbH)

In the plasticating unit, the material is melted and mixed by an internal batch mixer or a roll-mill before it is fed between the nip of the first two rolls. Here, the first pair of rolls control the feeding rate, while subsequent rolls in the calender calibrate the sheet thickness. Most calender systems have four rolls as does the one in Fig. 8.1, which is an inverted L- or F-type system. Other typical roll arrangements are shown in Fig. 8.2. After the main calender, the sheet can be passed through a secondary calendering operation for embossing. The sheet is then passed through a series of chilling rolls where it is cooled from both sides in an alternating fashion. After cooling, the film or sheet is wound.

   One of the major concerns in a calendering system is generating a film or sheet with a uniform thickness distribution with tolerances as low as ± 0.005 mm. To achieve this, the dimensions of the rolls must be precise. It is also necessary to compensate for roll bowing resulting from high pressures in the nip region. Roll bowing is a structural problem that can be mitigated by placing the rolls in a slightly crossed pattern, rather than completely parallel, or by applying moments to the roll ends to counteract the separating forces in the nip region.

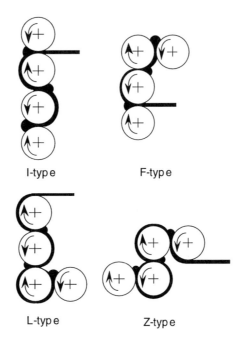

I-type   F-type

L-type   Z-type

Figure 8.2 Calender arrangements

ANALYSIS OF CALENDERING

Calendering can be modeled by assuming steady state, laminar flow and isothermal conditions. Such an analysis is presented by Middleman [2] and the main results are shown here. Assuming a power-law viscosity model given by

$$\eta = m|\dot\gamma|^{n-1} = m_0 e^{-a(T-T_0)}|\dot\gamma|^{n-1} \tag{8.1}$$

and the notation presented in the schematic shown in Fig. 8.3, the maximum pressure in the nip region can be calculated using

$$p_{max} = m\sqrt{\frac{2R}{h_0}}P(n) \tag{8.2}$$

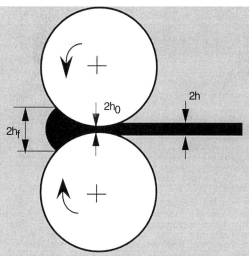

Figure 8.3 Schematic of the calendering process

where $P(n)$ is presented in Fig. 8.4[2]. The roll separating force caused by the pressure distribution between the nip can be calculated using

$$f = m \left(\frac{v}{h_0} \right)^n RWF(n) \tag{8.3}$$

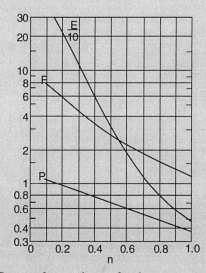

Figure 8.4 Pressure, force, and power functions versus power-law index

where W is the width of the sheet between the rolls and the quantity $F(n)$ can be found in Fig. 8.4[2]. The power transmitted to the sheet between the nips can also be calculated using

$$\dot{S} = mv^2 \left(\frac{v}{h_0}\right)^{n-1} W \sqrt{\frac{R}{h_0}} E(n) \tag{8.4}$$

where $E(n)$ is presented in Fig. 8.4 [2].

The sheet thickness, $2h$, as it emerges from the rolls is also a function of the power-law index and is presented in Fig. 8.5 for a system with a large amount of material accumulated at the entrance of the nip region. For the case where a finite sheet of thickness $2h_{feed}$ is fed through the nip region, the thickness of the film or sheet can be calculated using the curves presented in Fig. 8.6 [3].

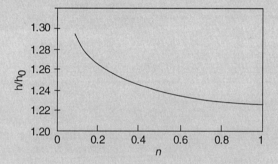

Figure 8.5 Sheet thickness as a function of power-law index for a large reservoir
thickness

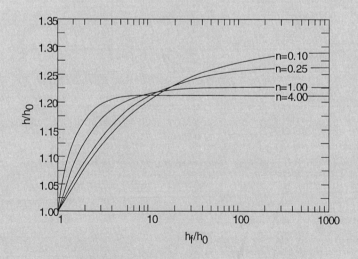

Figure 8.6 Sheet thickness as a function of upstream reservoir thickness for various
power-law indices

8.2 Coating

In coating a liquid film is continuously deposited on a moving, flexible or rigid substrate. Coating is done on metal, paper, photographic films, audio and video tapes, and adhesive tapes. Typical coating processes include *wire coating, dip coating, knife coating, roll coating, slide coating*, and *curtain coating*.

In wire coating, a wire is continuously coated with a polymer melt by pulling the wire through an extrusion die. The polymer resin is deposited onto the wire using the drag flow generated by the moving wire and sometimes a pressure flow generated by the back pressure of the extruder. The process is schematically depicted in Fig. 8.7.* The second normal stress differences, generated by the high shear deformation in the die, help keep the wire centered in the annulus [4].

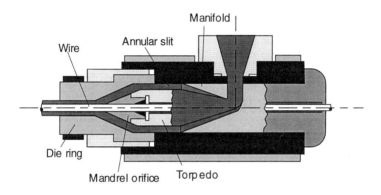

Figure 8.7 Wire coating process

Dip coating is the simplest and oldest coating operation. Here, a substrate is continuously dipped into a fluid and withdrawn with one or both sides coated with the fluid. Dip coating can also be used to coat individual objects that are dipped and withdrawn from the fluid. The fluid viscosity and density and the speed and angle of the surface determine the coating thickness.

Knife coating, depicted in Fig. 8.8, consists of metering the coating material onto the substrate from a pool of material, using a fixed rigid or flexible knife. The knife can be normal to the substrate or angled and the bottom edge can be flat or tapered. The thickness of the coating is nearly half the gap between the knife edge and the moving substrate or web. A major advantage of a knife edge coating system is its simplicity and relatively low maintenance.

Roll coating consists of passing a substrate and the coating simultaneously through the nip region between two rollers. The physics governing this process is similar to calendering, except that the fluid adheres to both the substrate and the opposing roll. The

---

* Other wire coating processes extrude a tubular sleeve which adheres to the wire via stretching and vacuum. This is called tube coating.

coating material is a low viscosity fluid, such as a polymer solution or paint and, is picked up from a bath by the lower roll and applied to one side of the substrate. The thickness of the coating can be as low as a few μm and is controlled by the viscosity of the coating liquid and the nip dimension. This process can be configured as either forward roll coating for co-rotating rolls or reverse roll coating for counter-rotating rolls (Fig. 8.9). The reverse roll coating process delivers the most accurate coating thicknesses.

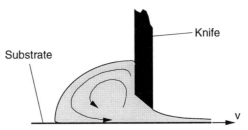

Figure 8.8 Schematic of a knife coating process

FILM THICKNESS IN FORWARD ROLL COATING

Using the nomenclature in Fig. 8.9, the thickness ratio of the film traveling with the rolls after they split can be calculated using [5]

$$\frac{T_2}{T_1} = \left(\frac{U_2}{U_1}\right)^E \tag{8.5}$$

where the exponent E is related to the shear thinning effect of the polymer melt. Figure 8.10 [5] presents E as a function of the power-law index.

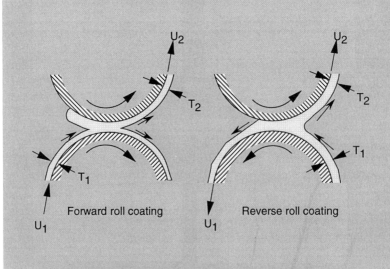

Figure 8.9 Schematic of forward and reverse roll coating processes

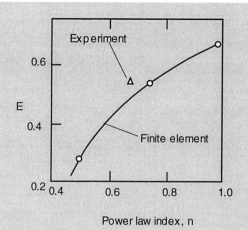

Figure 8.10 Constant E for Eq. (8.5) used to compute coating thickness in forward roll coating

RIBBING IN ROLL COATING

A defect that often forms during roll coating is caused by the ribbing instability. Here, sinusoidal waves across the web form, leaving so called rake lines in the moving direction of the substrate. Figure 8.11[5] presents the critical capillary number, which determines the onset of instabilities during forward roll coating as a function of roll geometry. The capillary number in Fig. 8.11 is defined by

$$Ca = \frac{\mu \bar{v}}{\sigma_s} \tag{8.6}$$

where μ is the viscosity of the coating fluid, $\bar{v}$ is the average roll speed, and σ_s is the surface tension of the fluid in air.

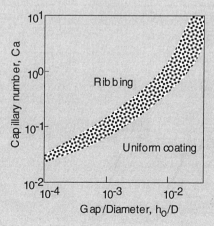

Figure 8.11 Critical capillary number for the onset of ribbing instabilities

FILM THICKNESS IN REVERSE ROLL COATING

Using the nomenclature used in Fig. 8.9, the film thickness in a reverse roll coating operation can be computed using the graph presented in Fig. 8.12 [5].

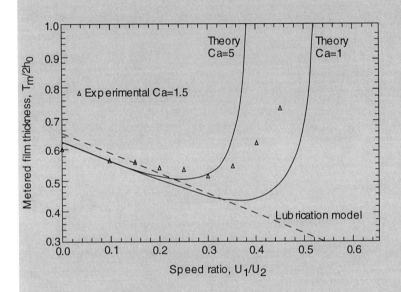

Figure 8.12 Film thickness versus roll speed ratio for various capilary numbers

Here, the capillary number is calculated using

$$Ca = \frac{\mu U_2}{\sigma_s} \tag{8.7}$$

where U_2 is the speed of the applicator roll. The figure shows how well theory agrees with experiments.

Slide coating and curtain coating, schematically depicted in Fig. 8.13, are commonly used to apply multi-layered coatings. However, curtain coating has also been widely used to apply single layers of coatings to cardboard sheet. In both methods, the coating fluid is pre-metered.

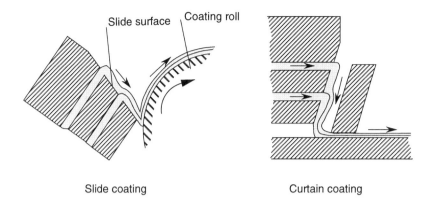

Figure 8.13 Slide and curtain coating

8.3 Processing Reactive Polymers

Reactive polymers, such as thermosets, undergo a chemical reaction during solidification. In processing, thermosets are often grouped into three distinct categories, namely those that undergo a *heat activated cure,* those dominated by a *mixing activated cure*, and those activated by the absorption of humidity or ultra violet radiation. Examples of heat activated thermosets are phenolics; examples of mixing activated cure are epoxy resins and polyurethane. Similarly to thermoplastics, thermosets either cure via *condensation polymerization* or *addition polymerization.*

Condensation polymerization is the growth process that results from combining two or more monomers with reactive end-groups, and leads to by-products such as alcohol, water and acid. The by-product of the reaction when making phenolics is water. Another well known example of a thermoset that cross links via condensation polymerization is the co-polymerization of unsaturated polyester with styrene molecules, also called free radical reaction, as shown in Fig. 8.14. The molecules contain several carbon-carbon double bonds which act as cross linking sites during curing. An example of the resulting network after the chemical reaction is shown in Fig. 8.15.

No matter which category of thermoset, its curing reaction can be described by the reaction between two chemical groups denoted by A and B which link two segments of a polymer chain. The reaction can be followed by tracing the concentration of unreacted As or Bs, C_A or C_B, respectively. If the initial concentrations of As and Bs are defined as C_{Ao} and C_{Bo}, the degree of cure can be described as

$$c = \frac{C_{Ao} - C_A}{C_{Ao}} \tag{8.8}$$

The degree of cure or conversion, c, equals zero when there has been no reaction and equals one when all As have reacted and the reaction is complete. It is difficult to monitor reacted and unreacted As and Bs during the curing reaction of a thermoset polymer. However, the heat released during curing can be used to monitor the conversion, c. When small samples of an unreacted thermoset polymer are placed in a differential scanning calorimeter (DSC), each at a different temperature, every sample releases nearly the same amount of heat, Q_T. This occurs because every cross link that occurs during a reaction releases a little heat. For example, Fig. 8.16 [6] shows the heating rate during isothermal cure of a vinyl ester at various temperatures.

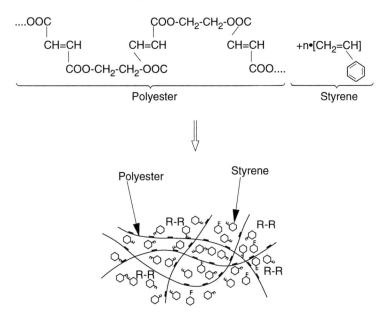

Figure 8.14   Symbolic and schematic representations of uncured unsaturated polyester

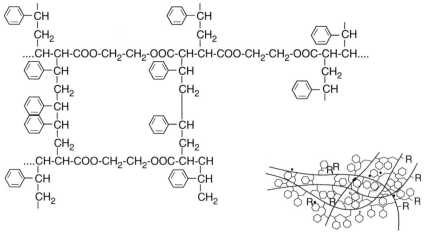

Figure 8.15   Symbolic and schematic representations of cured unsaturated polyester

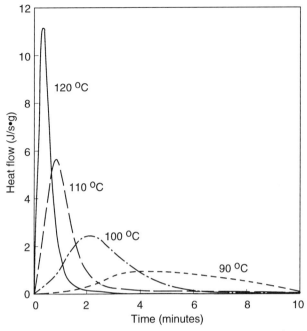

Figure 8.16 DSC scan of the isothermal curing reaction of vinyl ester at various temperatures

CURING REACTION MODELS

The degree of cure of a thermoset resin can be defined by the following relation

$$c = \frac{Q}{Q_T} \tag{8.9}$$

where Q is the heat released up to an arbitrary time t. DSC data is commonly fitted to empirical models that accurately describe the curing reaction. Hence, the rate of cure can be described by the exotherm, $\dot{Q}$ and the total heat released during the curing reaction, Q_T. The curing kinetics for many heat activated cure materials, such as vinyl esters and unsaturated polyesters, can be described fairly well using the Kamal-Sourour Model [7] given by

$$\frac{dc}{dt} = \frac{\dot{Q}}{Q_T} = \left(a_1 e^{-\frac{b_1}{RT}} + a_2 e^{-\frac{b_2}{RT}} c^m \right) (1-c)^n \tag{8.10}$$

where the six constants can be fit to DSC data.

On the other hand, mixing activated cure materials such as polyurethanes instantly start releasing exothermic heat after the mixture of its two components. A model that accurately fits this behavior is the *Castro-Macosko Curing Model* [8]:

$$\frac{dc}{dt} = k_0 e^{-\frac{E}{RT}}(1-c)^2 \tag{8.11}$$

HEAT TRANSFER DURING CURE

A well-known problem in thermoset components with thick sections is that the exothermic reaction encountered during curing leads to significant temperature rises within the material that may cause thermal degradation. A quick way of estimating the maximum temperature rise that can occur during curing is by using the adiabatic temperature rise given by

$$\Delta T = \frac{Q_T}{C_p} \tag{8.12}$$

where Q_T is the total heat released during reaction and C_p is the specific heat of the resin. Figure 8.17 is a plot of the time to reach 80% cure versus part thickness for various mold temperatures. The shaded area represents the conditions at which the internal temperature within the part exceeds 200 °C as a result of the exothermic reaction. A total heat of reaction of 84,000 J/kg was used in these calculations.

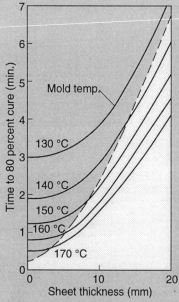

Figure 8.17 Cure times versus plate thickness for various mold temperatures (Shaded region represents the conditions at which thermal degradation can occur [9])

8.4 Compression Molding

Compression molding is widely used in the automotive industry to produce parts that are large, thin, lightweight, strong, and stiff. It is also used in the household goods and electrical industries. Compression molded parts are formed by squeezing a glass fiber reinforced charge inside a mold cavity, as depicted in Fig. 8.18. The matrix can be either a thermoset or thermoplastic. The most common matrix used to manufacture compression molded articles is unsaturated polyester sheet reinforced with glass fibers, known as sheet molding compound (SMC).

The 25 mm long reinforcing fibers are randomly oriented in the plane of the sheet and make up for 20-30% of the molding compound's volume fraction. A schematic diagram of an SMC production line is depicted in Fig. 8.19 [10]. When producing SMC, the chopped glass fibers are sandwiched between two carrier films previously coated with unsaturated polyester-filler matrix. A fiber reinforced thermoplastic charge is often called a glass mat reinforced thermoplastic (GMT) charge. The most common GMT matrix is polypropylene.

During processing of thermoset charges, the SMC blank is cut from a preformed roll and is placed between heated cavity surfaces. Generally, the mold is charged with 1 to 4 layers of SMC, each layer about 3 mm thick, which initially cover about half the mold cavity's surface. During molding, the initially randomly oriented glass fibers orient, leading to anisotropic properties in the finished product. When processing GMT charges, the preforms are cut and heated between radiative heaters. Once heated, they are placed inside a cooled mold that rapidly closes and squeezes the charges before they cool and solidify.

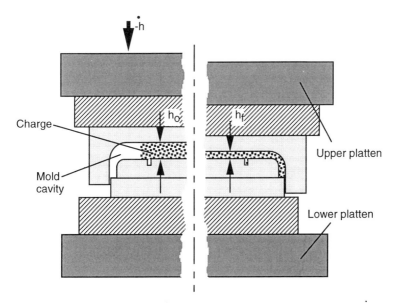

Figure 8.18 Compression molding process (h_0 = charge thickness, h_f = part thickness, and $\dot{h}$ = closing speed)

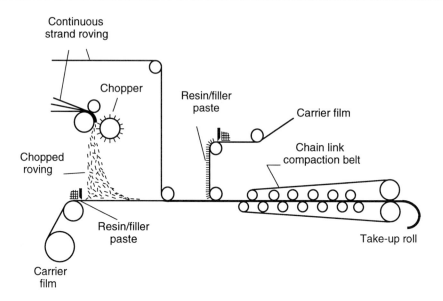

Figure 8.19 SMC production line

One of the main advantages of the compression molding process is the low fiber attrition during processing. Here, relatively long fibers can flow in the melt without the fiber damage common during plastication and cavity filling in injection molding.

An alternate process is injection-compression molding. Here, a charge is injected through a large gate followed by a compression cycle. The material used in the injection compression molding process is called bulk molding compound (BMC), which is reinforced with shorter fibers, generally 1 cm long, with an unsaturated polyester matrix. The main benefit of injection compression molding over compression molding is automation. The combination of injection and compression molding leads to lower degrees of fiber orientation and fiber attrition compared to injection molding.

As in any polymer process, in compression molding there is a direct relationship between deformation and final orientation in the part. Figure 8.20 depicts the fiber orientation distributionn within a plate were the initial charge coverage was 33% [11]. Such distribution functions are very common in compression or transfer molding and lead to high degrees of anisotropy throughout a product. To illustrate the effect of fiber orientation on material properties of the final part, Fig. 8.21 [12] shows how the deformation and resulting orientation from 33, 50, 66 and 100% mold coverage affects the stiffness of the plate.

Similar to injection molding, today, there are commercially available codes that can be used to predict mold filling, fiber orientation and warpage of compression molded parts. To predict fiber orientation in realistic parts, the Folgar–Tucker [13] model has been implemented into commercially available compression mold filling simulation programs. The predicted fiber orientation distribution field for a compression molded automotive fender is shown in Fig. 8.22 [14].

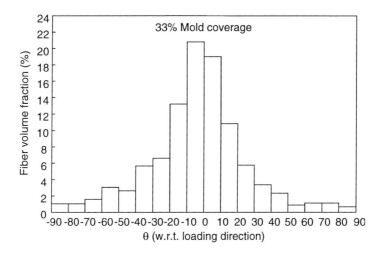

Figure 8.20 Measured fiber orientation distribution histogram in a plate with 33% initial mold coverage and extensional flow during mold filling.

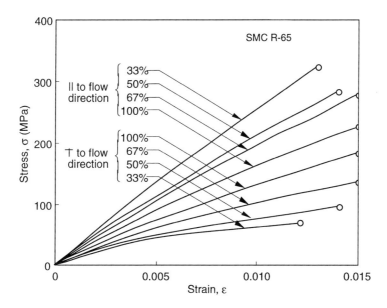

Figure 8.21   Stress-strain curves of 65% glass by volume SMC for various degrees of deformation.

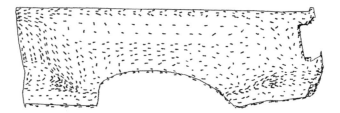

Figure 8.22   Fiber orientation distribution in a compression molded automotive fender.

To calculate the residual stress development during the manufacturing process, and shrinkage and warpage of the finished product commercially available programs use models where the heat transfer equation is coupled to the stress–strain analysis through constitutive equations. Figure 8.23 compares the mold geometry with the part geometry for the truck fender shown in Fig.8.22, after mold removal and cooling, computed using numerical models[15].

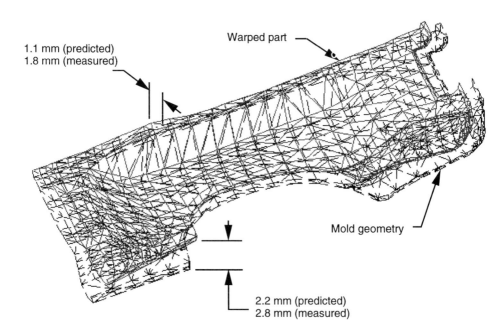

Figure 8.23   Simulated displacements of an automotive body panel. Displacements were magnified by a factor of 20.

8.5 Foaming

In foam or a foamed polymer, a cellular or porous structure has been generated through the addition and reaction of *physical* or *chemical blowing agents*. The basic steps of foaming are cell nucleation, expansion or cell growth, and cell stabilization. Nucleation occurs when, at a given temperature and pressure, the solubility of a gas is reduced, leading to saturation, expelling the excess gas to form a bubble. Nucleating agents, such as powdered metal oxides, are used for initial bubble formation. The bubbles reach an equilibrium shape when their inside pressure balances their surface tension and surrounding pressures. The cells formed can be completely enclosed (closed cell) or can be interconnected (open cell).

A physical foaming process is one where a gas such as nitrogen or carbon dioxide is introduced into the polymer melt. Physical foaming also occurs after heating a melt that contains a low boiling point fluid, causing it to vaporize. For example, the heat-induced volatilization of low-boiling point liquids, such as pentane and heptane, is used to produce polystyrene foams. Also, foaming occurs during volatilization from the exothermic reaction of gases produced during polymerization such as the production of carbon dioxide during the reaction of isocyanate with water. Physical blowing agents are added to the plasticating zone of the extruder or molding machine. The most widely used physical blowing agent is nitrogen. Liquid blowing agents are often added to the polymer in the hopper of the plasticating unit.

Chemical blowing agents are usually powders introduced in the hopper of the molding machine or extruder. Chemical foaming occurs when the blowing agent thermally decomposes, releasing large amounts of gas. The most widely used chemical polyolefin blowing agent is azodicarbonamide.

In mechanical foaming, a gas dissolved in a polymer expands upon reduction of the processing pressure.

The foamed structures commonly generated are either homogeneous foams or integral foams. Figure 8.24 [16] presents the various types of foams and their corresponding characteristic density distributions. In integral foam, the unfoamed skin surrounds the foamed inner core. This type of foam can be achieved during injection molding and extrusion and it replaces the sandwiched structure also shown in Fig. 8.24.

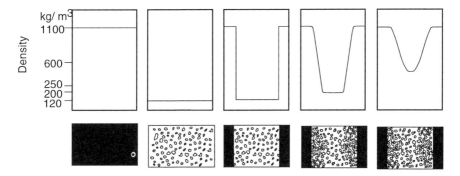

Figure 8.24 Schematic of various foam structures

8.6 Rotational Molding

Rotational molding is used to make hollow objects. In rotational molding, a carefully measured amount of powdered polymer, typically polyethylene, is placed in a mold. The mold is then closed and placed in an oven where the mold turns about two axes as the polymer melts, as depicted in Fig. 8.25. During heating and melting, which occur at oven temperatures between 250 and 450 °C, the polymer is deposited evenly on the mold's surface. To ensure uniform thickness, the axes of rotation should not coincide with the centroid of the molded product. The mold is then cooled and the solid part is removed from the mold cavity. The parts can be as thick as 1 cm, and still be manufactured with relatively low residual stresses. The reduced residual stress and the controlled dimensional stability of the rotational molded product depend in great part on the cooling rate after the mold is removed from the oven. A mold that is cooled too fast yields warped parts. Usually, a mold is first cooled with air to start the cooling slowly, followed by a water spray for faster cooling.

The main advantages of rotational molding over blow molding are the uniform part thickness and the low cost involved in manufacturing the mold. In addition, large parts such as play structures or kayaks can be manufactured more economically than with injection molding or blow molding. The main disadvantage of the process is the long cycle time for heating and cooling of the mold and polymer.

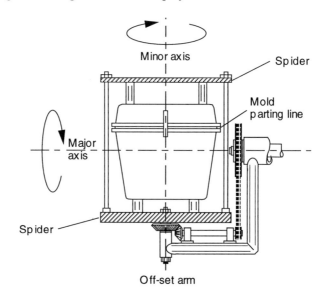

Figure 8.25 Schematic of the rotational molding process

Figure 8.26 presents the air temperature inside the mold in a typical rotational molding cycle for polyethylene powders [17]. The process can be divided into six distinct phases:

(1)   Induction or initial air temperature rise
(2)   Melting and sintering
(3)   Bubble removal and densification
(4)   Pre-cooling
(5)   Crystallization of the polymer melt
(6)   Final cooling

The induction time can be significantly reduced by pre-heating the powder, and the bubble removal and cooling stage can be shortened by pressurizing the material inside the mold. The melting and sintering of the powder during rotational molding depends on the rheology and geometry of the particles. This phenomenon was studied in depth by Bellehumeur and Vlachopoulos [18].

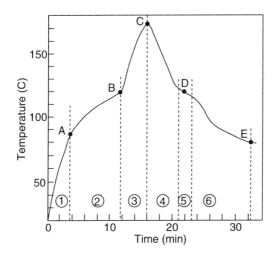

Figure 8.26 Typical air temperature in the mold while rotomolding polyethylene parts

ROTATIONAL MOLDING CYCLE TIME

The cycle time of the rotational molding process is governed by the time it takes to heat and cool the mold and the polymer. Since the mass of the polymer is negligible compared to the mass of the mold, the temperature can be estimated using

$$\left(\frac{T_f - T}{T_f - T_0}\right) = e^{-\frac{hA}{mC_p}t} \tag{8.13}$$

where T is temperature, T_f is the oven temperature (or cooling medium during cooling), T_0 is the initial temperature, h is the convective heat transfer coefficient, A is the outside surface area of the mold, C_p is the specific heat of the mold material, m is the mass of the mold and t is time.

Examples

8.1 A 10 mm thick PVC sheet is fed through a calender formed by 300 mm diameter, 2 meter long rolls, separated by a 5 mm gap. What is the final sheet thickness, and what is the roll separating force if the rolls turn at 60 rpm?

Material data: $m = 17,000 \ Pa - s^n$ and $n = 0.26$.

Since a sheet of finite thickness is fed to the calender we must use Fig. 8.6 to determine h. If we take an approximate power-law index of 0.25 and $h_f / h_0 = 2$, we read $h / h_0 = 1.085$, which results in a sheet thickness of 5.42 mm.

Next, we compute the roll separating force using Eq. (8.3) along with Fig. 8.4. Figure 8.4 gives $F(0.25) = 5$, so that

$$f = 17,000 \left(\frac{20(1/60)(2\pi)(0.15)}{0.0025} \right)^{0.26} (0.15)(2)(5) = 89.6 \ MN$$

Problems

8.1 For the PVC calendering in Example 8.1, determine the roll separation which results in a sheet thickness of 5 mm.

8.2 For the PVC calendering in Example 8.1, determine the maximum pressure between the rolls and the power required to drive the system.

8.3 A PVC calendering system similar to the one presented in Example 8.1 receives the material in a large roll, leading to a large reservoir. How much power is required to drive the system and what is the roll separating force if a 5 mm thick sheet is required?

8.4 What is the metered HDPE film thickness of a reverse roll coating system with 300 mm diameter rolls? Roll 1 rotates at 30 rpm and roll 2 at 90 rpm. The power-law index of HDPE is 0.41 and the surface tension of HDPE in air is 0.0265 N/m.

8.5 Will there be any ribbing instabilities in a polypropylene reverse roll coating operation where both rolls rotate at 120 rpm? The power-law index of PP is 0.38, and the surface tension of PP in air is 0.0208 N/m.

8.6 Plot the DSC output when measuring the exothermic reaction in an unsaturated polyester for a fixed temperature of 120 °C. Use the following properties:

$$a_1 = 4.9x10^{14} \ s^{-1}, \ a_2 = 6.2x10^5 \ s^{-1},$$
$$b_1 = 140 \ kJ / gmol, \ b_2 = 51 \ kJ / gmol$$
$$m = 1.3, \ n = 2.7, \ Q_T = 84 \ KJ / kg, \ R = 8.314 \ J / gmol / K$$
$$\rho = 1900 \ kg / m^3, \ C_p = 1000 \ J / kg / K, \ k = 0.53 \ W / m / K$$

8.7 For the unsaturated polyester data presented in Problem 8.6, plot the exothermic reaction as the temperature is ramped from 20 °C to 150 °C, at a rate of 5 K/min, 10 K/min and 20 K/min.

8.8 What maximum possible temperature change can the unsaturated polyester of Problem 8.6 undergo during processing ?

References

1. Menges, G., *Einführung in die Kunststoffverarbeitung*, Hanser Publishers (1986), Munich
2. Middleman, S., *Fundamentals of Polymer Processing*, McGraw-Hill Book Company (1977), New York
3. Brazinsky, I., H.F. Cosway, C.F. Valle, Jr., R.C. Jones, and V. Story, *J. Applied Polym. Sci.* (1970), *14*, 2771
4. Tadmor, Z., and R.B. Bird, *Polym.Eng.Sci.* (1973), *14*, 124
5. Coyle, D.J., *Moderm Coating and Drying Technology*, Chapter 3, E. Cohen and E. Gutoff, Eds., VCH (1992), New York
6. Palmese, G.R., O. Andersen, and V.M. Karbhari, *Advanced Composites X: Proceedings of the 10th Annual ASM/ESD Advance Composites Conference*, Dearborn, MI, ASM International (1994), Material Park
7   Kamal, M.R., S. Sourour, *Polym. Eng. Sci.* (1973), *13*, 59
8. Macosko, C.W., *RIM Fundamentals of Reaction Injection Molding*, Hanser Publishers (1989), Munich
9. Barone, M.R. and Caulk, D.A., *Int. J. Heat Mass Transfer* (1979), *22* , 1021
10. Denton, D.L, *The Mechanical Properties of an SMC-R50 Composite* (1979), Owens-Corning Fiberglas Corporation
11. Lee, C.-C., F. Folgar, and C.L. Tucker III, *J. Eng. Ind.* (1984), 186
12. Jackson, W.C., S.G. Advani, and C.L. Tucker III, *J. Comp. Mat.* (1986), *20*, 539
13. Folgar, F. and C.L. Tucker, *J. Reinf. Plast. Comp.* (1984), *3*,98
14. Gramann, P.J., E.M. Sun, and T.A. Osswald, *SPE 52nd Antec,* (1994)
15. CADPRESS™, The Madison Group:PPRC (1998), Madison, WI
16. Shutov, F.A., *Integral/Structural Polymer Foams*, Springer-Verlag (1986), Berlin
17. Crawford, R.J., *Rotational Molding of Plastics*, Research Studies Press (1992), Somerset
18. Bellehumeur, C.T., and J. Vlachopoulos, *SPE 56th Antec,* (1998)

Appendix

Appendices A1 to A5 use the polymer processing concepts covered in this book in a laboratory setting. The five laboratories included here are: extrusion, injection molding, blow molding, thermoforming, and film blowing. These laboratory procedures are written in general terms, and apply to most polymer processing equipment. Each laboratory presents sets of sample data that can be used to compare with your own, or as ersatz data for equipment not available in your facilities.

In most laboratory settings the equipment is much smaller than in industry. Therefore, scale-up must be done when translating learned concepts from the laboratory to an industrial scenario. Table A [1] is an example of scale-up or scale-down factors for polymer extruders where the rate of deformation, and therefore, the viscous dissipation is maintained constant.

Table A. Common Scaling Factors for Extruders [1]

Dimension	Extruder	Scaled Extruder
Diameter	D_1	D_2
Channel width	w_1	$w_2 = w_1(D_2/D_1)$
Channel depth	h_1	$h_2 = h_1(D_2/D_1)^{0.5}$
Screw speed	n_1	$n_2 = n_1(D_1/D_2)^{0.5}$
Output rate	$\dot{m}_1$	$\dot{m}_2 = \dot{m}_1(D_2/D_1)^2$
Shear rate	$\dot{\gamma}_1$	$\dot{\gamma}_2 = \dot{\gamma}_1$
Residence time	t_1	$t_2 = t_1(D_2/D_1)^{0.5}$
Power	P_1	$P_2 = P_1(D_2/D_1)^{2.5}$

Appendix A6 includes transport phenomena equations commonly used when deriving governing equations in polymer processing. For your reference several material property tables are given in Appendix A7.

References

1. Rauwendaal, C., *Polymer Extrusion*, Hanser Publishers (1990), Munich

A1 Extrusion Laboratory

The primary concern in an extrusion operation is maximizing throughput while maintaining product homogeneity, without generating excessive viscous dissipation. A constant mass throughput must also be maintained to achieve a product of uniform cross section.

A1.1 Objective

The objective of this laboratory is to determine the screw and die characteristic curves, and power requirement, for an HDPE by varying the screw speed and the valve restriction at the end of the extruder.* The temperature distribution at the screw tip and the pressure distribution along the barrel helps visualize the physical processes of extrusion.

A1.2 Laboratory Equipment

A1.2.1 Extruder

This laboratory examines the extrusion process with the Extrudex ED-N-45-25D extruder depicted in Fig.A1.1. This is a 45 mm diameter extruder with an L/D of 25. The screw in the extruder is the plasticating screw described in Table A1.1. Although the general principles in this laboratory apply to all extruders, individual running instructions for your machine must also be followed.

Table A1.1 Screw geometry

Section	Length	Depth (mm)
Feed section	8D	7
Melting section	11D	7-3
Metering section	6D	3

The extruder used in this experiment has an adjustable torpedo die which simulates dies of different restriction. In the notation used below, 0/0 (turns/degrees) implies a closed valve, equivalent to closed discharge. The extruder comes equiped with a series of pressure transducers and thermocouples along the barrel and in the die. They are located at 12D, 16D, 20D, 22D, and 25D. A zero pressure is assumed at 5D. Temperature

---

* **Caution:** The high temperatures associated with extrusion can injure. Do not manipulate the
parameters and components of the extruder unles so instructed. Wear safety glasses
when in the laboratory.

profiles across the barrel are measured with 5 thermocouples in the radial direction located 2D after the end of the screw.

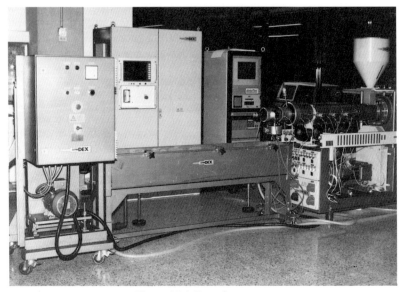

Figure A1.1 Extrusion set-up

A1.2.2 Material

The experiments presented here were all performed with an HDPE. The HDPE has a power-law index, n, of 0.41 and a consistency index, m, of 16,600 Pa-s^n at a temperature of 210 °C.

A1.2.3 Utilities

A typical extruder employs electricity, water, and compressed air. The water cools the feed-throat near the hopper and the compressed air often cools the barrel in extruders without blowers. The extruder in this laboratory has blowers.
Before beginning check:

- that barrel zone temperatures have reached the set points indicated on the laboratory procedure handout
- that the hopper is about half full of plastic pellets

A1.3 Experimental Procedure

Initial Settings

The temperature settings in the different heating zones along the barrel must be held constant throughout the experiments. These settings are in Table A1.2.

Table A1.2 Heating zone temperature settings

Zone	Temperature (°C)
Feed section	160 and 170
Melting section	180 and 190
Metering section	200
Thermocomb section	200
Die	200

Step 1

Once the desired temperatures are reached, set the die to 10 turns 0 degrees (10/0). Set the screw speed to 30 rpm and measure the mass throughput by weighting the extrudate that emerges from the die in one minute. Record the following:

- Mass throughput, kg/hr
- Screw torque, N-m
- Temperature of the polymer at the screw tip, ° C
- Pressure profile along the barrel, bar

Step 2

Repeat Step 1 for 60, 90, and 120 rpm.

Step 3

Repeat Steps 1 and 2 with die settings of 3/180 and 2/180. Data collected for the experimental set-up and material described above are in Table A1.3.

Step 4

Plot the die and screw characteristic curves

Step 5

Plot the pressure profile along the barrel for all die restrictions at a screw speed of 90 rpm. Repeat for all screw speeds and for a die restriction of 2/180.

Step 6

Plot the temperature distribution at the screw tip for all die restrictions and a screw speed of 90 rpm. Repeat for all screw speeds and for a die restriction of 2/180.

Table A1.3 Data for single screw extruder.

N	X	$\dot{m}$	T	P1	P2	P3	P4	P5	T1	T2	T3	T4	T5
30	10/0	9.75	0.25	72	103	124	94	53	222	195	196	194	211
60	10/0	19.35	0.33	87	133	151	104	78	223	193	193	193	211
90	10/0	29.20	0.39	108	154	158	115	105	219	183	190	192	207
120	10/0	38.80	0.43	126	171	168	122	134	217	180	188	193	207

N	X	$\dot{m}$	T	P1	P2	P3	P4	P5	T1	T2	T3	T4	T5
30	3/180	9.00	0.25	140	176	182	112	71	234	198	198	196	223
60	3/180	17.95	0.33	173	224	217	130	91	232	195	196	195	219
90	3/180	26.75	0.39	200	254	241	151	118	229	190	194	196	216
120	3/180	35.65	0.43	225	280	257	161	151	227	178	195	199	214

N	X	$\dot{m}$	T	P1	P2	P3	P4	P5	T1	T2	T3	T4	T5
30	2/180	8.20	0.25	213	250	241	137	86	238	201	200	198	227
60	2/180	16.40	0.34	260	315	290	157	101	236	200	201	200	225
90	2/180	24.60	0.39	293	355	320	192	133	234	197	200	201	221
120	2/180	32.40	0.43	321	381	331	196	156	231	191	197	203	212

N = screw speed (rpm),   X = die opening (0/0 = closed discharge)
$\dot{m}$ = mass flow rate (kg/hour),   T = torque (N-m)
Pi = pressure along the screw (bars), Ti = temperatures in front of the screw (°C)

A2 Injection Molding Laboratory

A primary concern of the injection molder is to manufacture plastic parts with certain special dimensions. To achieve this one must apply an appropriate sequence of events, which varies with material, during the molding cycle.

A2.1 Objective

This laboratory examines the injection molding of polystyrene (PS). The student will examine the injection molding process, produce several test specimens, and investigate the effect of process variables on part quality and processability.[*] This laboratory aims to control the part dimensions by varying the pack/hold pressure and by changing the switchover point. The switchover point is when the injection molding machine switches from a constant injection screw speed to a constant injection pressure. These adjustments are depicted in Fig. A2.1, which relates the cycle to the screw position.

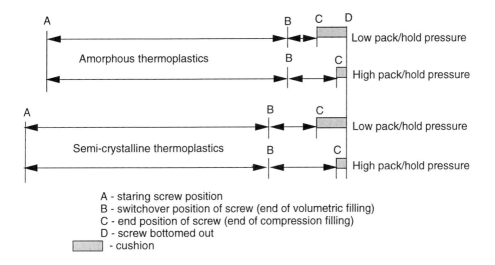

A - staring screw position
B - switchover position of screw (end of volumetric filling)
C - end position of screw (end of compression filling)
D - screw bottomed out
□ - cushion

Figure A2.1 Screw movement for amorphous and semi-crystalline thermoplastics

---

[*] **Caution:** The high temperatures associated with the injection molding machine can injure. Do not manipulate the parameters and components of the injection molding machine unless so instructed. Wear safety glasses when in the laboratory.

A2.2 Laboratory Equipment

A2.2.1 Injection Molder

In this example laboratory a Boy 22S injection molding machine, depicted in Fig. A2.2, is used. However, this laboratory applies to most injection molding machines and individual running instructions for the machine in your laboratory must be followed.

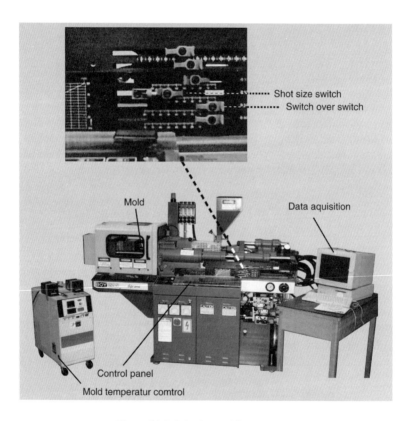

Figure A2.2   Injection molding machine

The mold used for these sample runs was for the flexural bar depicted in Fig. A2.3, and was equipped with two pressure transducers, one near the gate and the second at the end of the mold cavity. The pressure transducers are flush-mounted within the stationary half of the mold cavity that defines the flexural bar. Each pressure transducer must be calibrated before tests start. The pressure transducers are deployed inside the mold cavity to measure polymer pressure during filling, packing, and cooling.

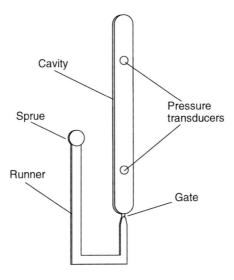

Figure A2.3   Schematic of the mold cavity

A2.2.2 Utilities

A typical injection molder uses electricity and water. The water cools the feed-throat by the hopper. Hydraulic oil is also used for this purpose.

First check that:

- the temperatures of the barrel zones should have reached the set points indicated on the laboratory procedure handout
- the hopper is about half full of plastic pellets
- the mold cavity is empty, which must be checked after every cycle

A2.3 Experimental Procedure

Semi-Automatic Operation:

To initiate operation:

- Press the pump motor start button on the control panel
- Turn the selector dial to the semi-automatic position
- Close the mold safety gate or press the mold close button on the bottom of the control panel. One cycle runs automatically, ending with the specimen ejection

- Ensure that the part has fallen out of the mold cavity. If necessary, carefully pull out the part
- To continue operation, open and close the mold safety gate or press the mold close button

To vary processing times or pressures press the buttons to increase or decrease the values.

To vary shot size or switchover point:

- The shot size switch is usually located below the barrel. An Allen wrench is used to loosen the screw. The shot size is adjusted using a thumb-wheel to slide the switch left or right. The screw must be re-tightened.

- The constant velocity/pressure switchover switch is also located below the barrel. Again, an Allen wrench is used to loosen the screw so the switch can be slid to the left or right. The screw must then be re-tightened.

Initial Settings

The initial base-line settings for all experiments should be:

- Mold temperature = 60 °C
- Melting zone temperature = 150 °C
- Metering zone temperature = 170 °C
- Nozzle temperature = 170 °C
- Shot size = 39 (machine specific units)
- Switchover = 7 (machine specific units)
- Injection speed = 25% of maximum
- Pack/hold pressure = 25% of maximum
- Highest injection pressure allowed = 80% of maximum
- Cooling time = 30 s
- Pack/hold time = 20 s

Step 1

With all the process parameters at their original set-points, observe the pressure trace during the process. Note the shape of the curve at the switchover point and the maximum pressure developed within the cavity. Then observe the cavity pressure traces when the switchover is varied by -2 and +5 from the original switchover value.

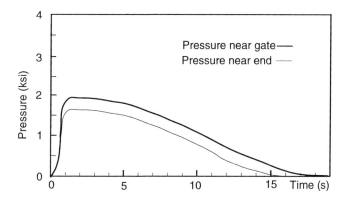

Figure A2.4 Pressure transducer readings with the original settings

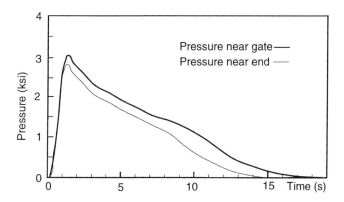

Figure A2.5 Pressure transducer readings with a switchover point at 5 (-2)

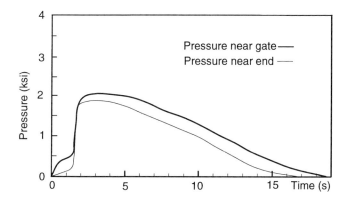

Figure A2.6 Pressure transducer readings with a switchover point at 12 (+7)

Step 2

With all process parameters at their original set-points (including the switchover value), observe what happens to the cavity pressure traces when the shot size is increased by +2 from the original value.

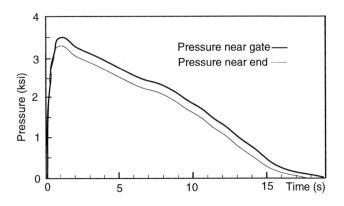

Figure A2.7 Pressure transducer readings with a shot size at 41 (+2)

Step 3

With the pack/hold pressure set at 40% (and the shot size back at its recommended setting), observe the cavity pressure traces as the pack/hold time is decreased in 5 s increments (stop at 5 s). Find acceptable pack/hold time by increasing it in increments of 5 s. Also note if the part becomes difficult to eject.

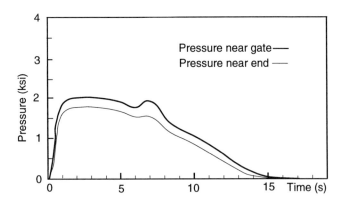

Figure A2.8 Pressure transducer readings with a pack/hold time of 5 s

Step 4

With a pack/hold pressure of 40% and the pack/hold time set as determined in the previous step, observe what happens to the ease of part ejection as the cooling time is lowered in 5 s increments (stop at 5 s or if part ejection becomes difficult). Set the cooling time to an acceptable value in increments of 5 s.

Step 5

With all settings at their optimized values, determine the influence of pack/hold pressure (at 10, 25, and 40%) on product thickness. Mold three samples at each set of conditions and measure the samples at two different distances from the gate. Sample data is in Table A2.1. Also, weigh the three bars for each set of conditions.

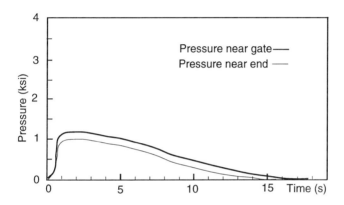

Figure A2.9 Pressure transducer readings with a pack/hold pressure setting at 10%

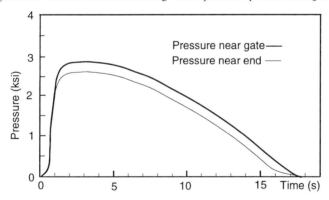

Figure A2.10 Pressure transducer readings with a pack/hold pressure setting at 40%

Step 6

With the time settings determined at the end of step 4 and a pack/hold pressure of 40%, determine ΔP_{fill}. Recall that ΔP_{fill} refers to the pressure loss between transducers 1 and 2 during volumetric filling. Conduct each run three times and record the pressure loss values observed on the data acquisition system. Then lower the mold temperature to

27 °C and run the 40% pack/hold pressure trial again. Allow 15 minutes for the mold temperature to equilibrate. The pressure transducers must now be re-calibrated. Note: Compare part thickness changes at mold temperatures of 60 °C and 27 °C.

Table A2.1 Sample thickness and weight.

Trial	Pressure (%)	Thickness (mm)		Weight (g)
		near gate	mold end	
1	10	3.140	3.114	5.08
2	10	3.140	3.116	5.09
3	10	3.136	3.116	5.08
1	25	3.150	3.136	5.12
2	25	3.144	3.142	5.11
3	25	3.144	3.136	5.11
1	40	3.180	3.168	5.17
2	40	3.176	3.164	5.16
3	40	3.178	3.168	5.17

A3 Blow Molding Laboratory

One of the primary concerns during blow molding is controlling wall thickness distribution within the final article. The ultimate goal can be to obtain a uniform wall thickness with a minimum of material. The wall thickness distribution of a blow molded article influences integrity, performance, and cost.

A3.1 Objective

This experiment demonstrates how several processing variables affect the product quality of a blow molded article, with particular emphasis on how these variables can influence the wall thickness uniformity within the molding.[*] By measuring the axial and circumferential wall thicknesses for several blow molded articles, the student can gain an understanding of the causes of non-uniform wall thicknesses.

A3.2 Laboratory Equipment

A3.2.1 Blow Molder

In the sample laboratory presented in this section a Rocheleau extrusion blow molding machine, depicted in Fig. A3.1, is used. The procedure described here applies to all extrusion blow molding equipment, however. Auto-timers regulate the time for each stage of the blow molding cycle during the automatic and semi-automatic modes.

A3.2.2 Utilities

The blow molder presented here uses electricity, water, and compressed air. Compressed air inflates the parison and ejects the molded article at the end of the cycle. The air pressure during inflation is controlled via a pressure gauge. Flow rate control valves control the ejector speed. Water is used for cooling.

Setting Screw Rotation Speed and Turn Time:

Before you start the blow molding operation you must set the screw rotation speed and time. At any given screw rotation speed, the screw must rotate enough to extrude the whole parison . The parison must reach just beyond the pinch point at the mold bottom just as the mold closes (Fig. A3.2). The parison must not be so long that material is wasted.

---

[*] **Caution:**   The high temperatures, high pressures, and moving components associated with the blow molding machine can seriously injure. Do not manipulate the parameters and components of the blow molding machine unless so instructed . Wear safety glasses when in the laboratory.

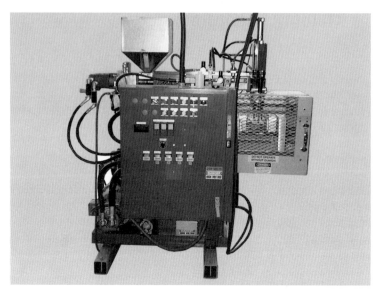

Figure A3.1 Blow molder

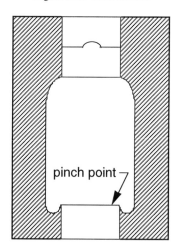

Figure A3.2 Schematic of the bottle mold

A3.3 Experimental Procedure

Manual Operation

Use the manual mode to determine an appropriate screw turn time.

1. Turn the cycle dial to MANUAL and the eject dial to OFF.
2. Press and hold the SCREW TURN button.

3. Release the SCREW TURN button when the parison bottom reaches the mold pinch point.
4. Immediately press and hold the CLAMP button, then press and hold the BLOW button. Hold the BLOW button for the same time indicated on the blow timer.
5. Release the BLOW button but continue to hold the CLAMP button for the time indicated on the air exhaust timer.
6. Release the CLAMP button.
7. Turn the eject dial to DOWN to eject the molded article.

Materials

Two materials are examined. Start the experiment with the polymer that remains in the hopper.

Trial 1. HDPE at the following conditions
Temperature profile (barrel to nozzle): 190, 200, 210 and 210 °C
Blowing pressure: 2.5-2.75 bar (adjust the pressure regulator during the blowing step)

Trial 2. LDPE at the following conditions
Temperature profile (barrel to nozzle): 190, 200, 210 and 210 °C
Blowing pressure: 1.7 bar (adjust the pressure regulator during the blowing step)

Purging the Barrel

After you complete the experiment using one material, you must purge the barrel to introduce the next material.

• Empty the old material from the hopper
• Fill hopper with the new material
• Turn the screw to continously extrude a parison until the new material appears and the old material has been sufficiently purged.

Step 1

Repeat trials 1 through 2 with screw speeds of 30 and 80 rpm. The parison extrudes as you adjust the screw speed. Remove all of the extrudate from the nozzle once the proper screw speed is set.

Step 2

Check the time needed for extrusion by running the cycle and checking if the parison is properly pinched. However, fine tune the time setting to the nearest 0.5 s once the machine is running in the semi-automatic mode to minimize the trim waste. Starting points for screw turn time are approximately 10 s at a high rpm and 30 s at a low rpm.

Step 3

As soon as the process has been fine tuned, collect two blow molded bottles for each experimental trial. Make sure that you keep track of which side is which on the blow molded products. Record the actual screw rpm and extrusion time used for each experiment. As the parison is extruded through the annular die it will first swell, then sag. The swelling reflects the elasticity of the polymer melt and the sagging reflects the melt viscosity. Hence, polymers are often called viscoelastic. Swelling and sagging influence the product wall thickness, i.e. more swelling and less sagging will thicken the part, and *vice versa*. Note any difficulties encountered while running the trials.

Step 4

Measure the axial wall thickness distribution at five locations along opposite sides of each bottle (90° from the parting line and normal to the bottle surface). The thickness distribution in blow molded articles can be measured with a micrometer or electronically. Also record each bottle weight. Sample measurements are presented in Fig. A3.3.

Step 5

Continue to the next set of processing parameters, changing the material if necessary. Give the system enough time to re-equilibrate when changing the process temperatures. If changing materials, purge the material adequately with the new material. The screw rpm is controlled by a constant torque motor. While purging, note any changes in the screw rpm as the new material is fed into the screw. Once the material is completely purged, return to Step 1.

Step 6

Plot the thickness distribution for all cases. Explain thickness variations within each bottle and between experiments.

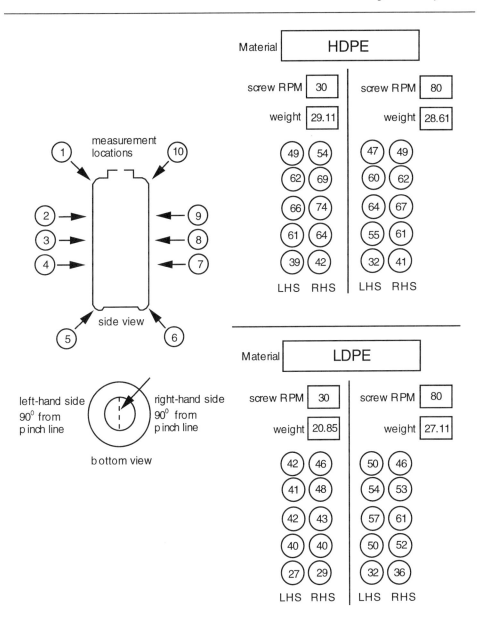

Figure A3.3 Sample measurements

A4 Thermoforming Laboratory

Thermoforming involves drawing a softened sheet of plastic into a mold cavity. To soften the sheet, its temperature is usually raised via radiant heat. Just before shaping, the sheet is positioned over the mold cavity. Wall thickness control and replicating cavity detail are two major concerns when manufacturing a plastic article this way. Vacuum, pressure, or mechanical assists can be used to optimize the shaping.

A4.1 Objective

This thermoforming laboratory aims to produce a thermoformed truncated cone with minimal variation in the thickness distribution. The sequence of events in this thermoforming laboratory starts with the motion of two platens – a lower one onto which a mold cavity is bolted and an upper one onto which a plug is bolted.[*] The operation can also involve the application of negative or positive pressures to the mold cavity. Furthermore, the speed at which these pressures are applied during the thermoforming process can be varied.

A4.2 Laboratory Equipment

A4.2.1 Thermoforming Machine

In this example laboratory a CAM thermoforming machine, depicted in Figs. A4.1 and A4.2, is used. Although the machine used in the laboratory is much smaller than the ones encountered in industry, it represents the process well. The control console includes the control switches for operation in manual and automatic modes. Before the laboratory, confirm that the set points for all switches agree with those indicated on the laboratory procedure.

Each forming valve (e.g., pre-blow and full vacuum) has a three position selector switch:

- off - valve disabled throughout the entire forming cycle
- on - valve enabled automatically during the forming cycle
- over-ride - valve enabled manually

The automatic action of the forming valves required for a specific thermoforming technique are controlled via platen positions, delay timers, and duration timers. In this experiment, only the full vacuum forming valve is used. This valve rapidly removes air

---

[*] **Caution**:   The high temperatures and pressures, and moving elements associated with the thermoforming machine seriously injure. Do not manipulate the parameters and components of the thermoforming machine unless so instructed. Be especially cautious of the feed car movement. Wear safety glasses when in the laboratory.

from the cavity which causes the sheet to draw against the cavity walls. The feedback temperature controller readily allows you to change the temperature set points of the oven.

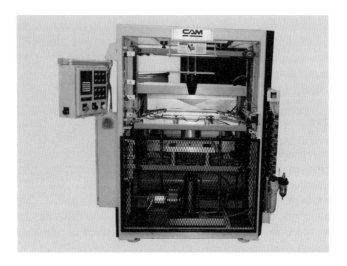

Figure A4.1 Thermoforming machine

Figure A4.2 Close-up of the clamps, mold, and plug assist of the thermoforming machine

A4.2.2 Utilities

Most thermoforming machines use electricity and compressed air. The compressed air is used in many areas of the process, such as the vacuum pump, the sheet clamps in the sled, the sled motion, and the platen motion.

A4.3 Experimental Procedure

Running a Cycle

Manual Operation

- Load a plastic sheet in the feed car

- Turn the switch to MANUAL if the manual indicator light is off

- Move the CLAMPS switch to CLOSE

- Move the FEED CAR switch to OVEN. Leave the sheet in the oven for the right amount of time. This depends on the sheet thickness. For the 2 mm (0.080") thick, high impact polystyrene sheet, the heating time is between 90 and 100 s

- Move the FEED CAR switch back to FORM

- Move the TOP PLATEN switch to CLOSE

- Move the MAIN VACUUM switch to OVER-RIDE for 10 seconds

- Turn the MAIN VACUUM switch off

- Move the TOP PLATEN switch back to OPEN

- Move the CLAMPS switch back to OPEN

  - Carefully remove the formed plastic sheet from the feed car

Automatic Operation:

- Confirm the set points for the forming valves on the control console

- Confirm the temperature set points, and wait for the temperature to stabilize if necessary

- Make necessary changes to the menus in the Operator Interface Unit

- Load a plastic sheet in the feed car

•Turn MODE switch to AUTO if the auto indicator light is off

•Simultaneously press the two cycle buttons on each side of the control panel

•When the cycle is complete, carefully remove the formed plastic sheet from the feed car

Material

High Impact Polystyrene (HIPS) sheets 2 mm (0.080") thick.

Trials

Three different thermoforming methods are examined during the thermoforming laboratory :

1. Vacuum thermoforming
2. Full plug-assist vacuum thermoforming
3. Partial plug-assist vacuum thermoforming

Although only a few thermoforming techniques are examined in this lab, there are many other variations used to produce thermoformed articles of uniform wall thickness. Besides vacuum and plug-assist, pre-blowing of sheet, vacuum bleeding of mold cavity, pressure forming of sheet, and forming of sheet onto a core rather than into a cavity are other methods used in thermoforming.

All trials are run with the oven temperature set a 260 °C. To raise the HIPS sheets to their appropriate forming temperatures requires a certain heating time.

Step 1

Run the HIPS trials according to the following menu settings, and ensure that you keep track of which side is the front of the thermoformed products :

Trial 1:   Set cycle time for heating sheet to 90 s
            Set delay time for applying full vacuum to 0 s

Trial 2:   Set cycle time for heating sheet to 100 s
            Set delay time for applying full vacuum to 3 s

Step 2

The thermoformed parts must be analyzed for their wall thickness distributions with an electronic or manual micrometer. Sample thickness data and location on the cone are shown in Fig. A4.3 and Table A4.1.

Step 3

The optimum settings for thermoforming should yield a cone with a constant wall thickness. Compare constant thickness cone to the measured values for each trial.

Step 4

Now try to thermoform a cone with an optimun wall thickness. Run at least 3 trials changing the delay time to appropriate values, measuring each cone until your wall thickness is the most uniform. For these trials:

• Set the sheet heating time to 95 s
• Set delay time for applying full vacuum between 0 and 3 s

Step 5

Visually inspect the parts for surface finish and dimensional accuracy and compare these for the different trials.

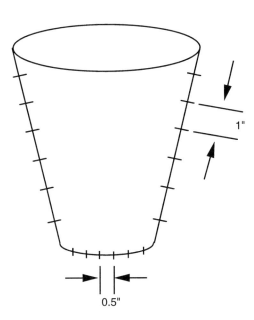

Figure A4.3 Cone locations for thickness measurements

Table A4.1 Thermoforming Laboratory Sample Thickness Data (mills)

	Trial 1	Trial 2	Trial 3	Trial 4	Trial 5
Heating time:	95	95	95	95	95
Delay time:	0	1	1.5	2	3
Cone:	70	75	57	51	46
(Ovenside)	48	58	47	43	36
	31	41	32	33	31
	15	23	23	28	39
	6	14	21	32	39
	4	9	21	28	20
	3	4	20	21	11
Edge:	2	2	12	10	11
Base:	2	3	15	11	15
	5	3	18	15	17
	3	4	23	20	19
	3	4	21	17	17
	2	3	17	13	13
Edge:	3	3	8	9	10
Cone:	3	4	18	21	12
(Far oven)	4	9	35	34	20
	6	21	28	30	37
	13	23	27	32	30
	30	39	36	27	28
	44	55	42	31	26
	74	74	50	50	47

A5 Film Blowing Laboratory

The primary concern in film blowing is to maximize the mechanical and optical properties and minimize the permeability. The varying process parameters are the draw-down ratio, the bubble pressure, the cooling rates, and hence the blow-up ratio.

A5.1 Objective

This laboratory examines film blowing of low density polyethylene using the film blowing tower shown in Fig. A5.1. The student must vary processing conditions such as take-up speed, bubble pressure and extruder mass throughput, and find the effect of these process variations on film thickness. The results can be presented on dimensionless graphs, such as Figs. 7.7 and 7.8, shown for the Newtonian case in Chapter 7.

A5.2 Laboratory Equipment

In this laboratory, a one inch Killion extruder is used along with a film blowing die and tower. The annular die, that extrudes a 0.5" diameter tube through a 0.015" slit, is attached to a cooling unit such as shown in Fig. A5.2. The film is blown into its final diameter above the die, collapsed by a system of guider rollers and pulled by 2 rollers at a known take-up speed. The material throughput is controlled using the extruder screw speed, the take-up speed by the roller speed and the internal bubble pressure using a valve connected to an air supply. The internal bubble pressure is measured using a water manometer. Under steady-state conditions, the air mass contained between the die and the rollers is constant and the air leakage is compensated by occasionally injecting air into the bubble. Cooling is generally achieved by forced convection from air blown through a ring just above the die.

A5.2.2 Utilities

The extruder uses electricity, water and compressed air. The water is used to cool the feed-throat area by the hopper and the compressed air is used, for extruders without blowers, to cool the barrel. The film blowing die and tower use electricity and compressed air.

First, check:

- that the temperatures of the barrel zones have reached the set points indicated on the laboratory procedure handout

- that the hopper is about half full of plastic pellets

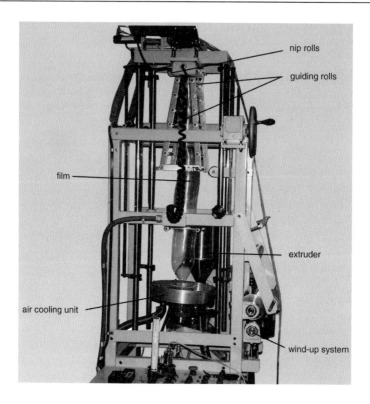

Figure A5.1 Film blowing tower

Figure A5.2 Detail of air cooling unit and film

A5.3 Experimental Procedure

Processing Conditions

Initial processing conditions:

Set the barrel heater temperatures to 160°C in feed section, 175°C in the transition zone and 175°C in the metering zone, and the die temperature to 115°C.

Step 1

- Once the heaters reach the desired temperature, set the screw speed to 30 rpm
- Take an old film that runs through the guider, the upper roller system (upper nip) and the lower roller system (lower nip) and stick it to the polymer melt emerging from the die.
- Start the upper roller system and close the rollers after the new extrudate goes through the nip. Use an initial roller speed of 3 feet/min.
- Close the lower nip, ensuring the lower and upper rollers have the same speed

Step 2

Slowly open the air valve until the bubble pressure reaches approximately 6 inches of water. After 20 seconds, when the bubble is fully developed from the die to the upper nip, decrease the bubble pressure to 0.5 inches of water. At the lower pressures, the micro-manometer is turned to the slant position, so the pressures can be read from the finer scale.

Step 3

Start the blower and adjust the speed to maintain a smooth bubble shape.

Step 4

Record the following data (Sample data is presented in Table A5.1):

- Mass flow rate
- Bubble diameter
- Take-up speed
- Bubble pressure
- Position of freezing line (position of stable bubble shape)

Step 5

Plot the blow-up ratio as a function of the thickness reduction as shown in the dimensionless graphs of Chapter 7. Use Fig. A5.3* to determine an average viscosity to non-dimensionalize the pressure with Eq. (7.9).

Step 6
Using the conditions given above, change the take-up speed to 10 and 25 feet/min. Plot the results.

Step 7

Using a take-up speed of 10 feet/min, change the bubble pressure to 0.2 and 1.5 inches of water.

Step 8

Using a take-up speed of 10 feet/min, decrease the screw speed and run internal bubble pressures of 0.2, 0.5 and 1.2 inches of water.

Table A5.1 Sample data

$\dot{m}$ (g/min)	D_f (in)	v_f (feet/min)	Δp (in H_2O)	Z (in)
27.8	15.0	3	0.5	9.0
27.9	13.5	10	0.5	6.5
27.5	13.5	25	0.5	8.5
27.8	13.5	10	0.2	11.5
27.6	15.0	10	1.5	4.5
10.2	13.0	10	0.2	6.5
10.6	15.0	10	0.5	5.5
10.7	15.0	10	1.2	4.0

----

* Meissner, J., *Rheol. Acta, 10* , 230, (1971).

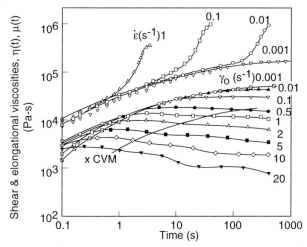

Figure A5.3 Development of elongational and shear viscosities during deformation for polyethylene samples.

A6 Transport Phenomena Equations

ENERGY EQUATION

The Energy Equation

$$\rho C_v \frac{DT}{Dt} = (\nabla \cdot k \nabla T) + \frac{1}{2}\mu(\dot{\underline{\underline{\gamma}}} : \dot{\underline{\underline{\gamma}}}) + \dot{Q}$$

The Energy Equation in Terms of Transport Properties

Rectangular coordinates (x,y,z):

$$\rho C_v\left(\frac{\partial T}{\partial t}+v_x\frac{\partial T}{\partial x}+v_y\frac{\partial T}{\partial y}+v_z\frac{\partial T}{\partial z}\right) = k\left(\frac{\partial^2 T}{\partial x^2}+\frac{\partial^2 T}{\partial y^2}+\frac{\partial^2 T}{\partial z^2}\right)$$
$$+ 2\mu\left(\left(\frac{\partial v_x}{\partial x}\right)^2+\left(\frac{\partial v_y}{\partial y}\right)^2+\left(\frac{\partial v_z}{\partial z}\right)^2\right)+\mu\left(\left(\frac{\partial v_x}{\partial y}+\frac{\partial v_y}{\partial x}\right)^2+\left(\frac{\partial v_x}{\partial z}+\frac{\partial v_z}{\partial x}\right)^2+\left(\frac{\partial v_y}{\partial z}+\frac{\partial v_z}{\partial y}\right)^2\right)+\dot{Q}$$

Cylindrical coordinates (r,θ,z):

$$\rho C_v\left(\frac{\partial T}{\partial t}+v_r\frac{\partial T}{\partial r}+\frac{v_\theta}{r}\frac{\partial T}{\partial \theta}+v_z\frac{\partial T}{\partial z}\right) = k\left(\frac{1}{r}\frac{\partial}{\partial r}\left(r\frac{\partial T}{\partial r}\right)+\frac{1}{r^2}\frac{\partial^2 T}{\partial \theta^2}+\frac{\partial^2 T}{\partial z^2}\right)$$
$$+ 2\mu\left(\left(\frac{\partial v_r}{\partial r}\right)^2+\left(\frac{1}{r}\left(\frac{\partial v_\theta}{\partial \theta}+v_r\right)\right)^2+\left(\frac{\partial v_z}{\partial z}\right)^2\right)$$
$$+ \mu\left(\left(\frac{\partial v_\theta}{\partial z}+\frac{1}{r}\frac{\partial v_z}{\partial \theta}\right)^2+\left(\frac{\partial v_z}{\partial r}+\frac{\partial v_r}{\partial z}\right)^2+\left(\frac{1}{r}\frac{\partial v_r}{\partial \theta}+r\frac{\partial}{\partial r}\left(\frac{v_\theta}{r}\right)\right)^2\right)+\dot{Q}$$

CONTINUITY EQUATION

Continuity Equation (Incompressible Fluids)

$$\nabla \cdot \underline{v} = 0$$

Rectangular coordinates

$$\frac{\partial v_x}{\partial x} + \frac{\partial v_y}{\partial y} + \frac{\partial v_z}{\partial z} = 0$$

Cylindrical coordinates (r,θ,z)

$$\frac{1}{r}\frac{\partial}{\partial r}(rv_r) + \frac{1}{r}\frac{\partial v_\theta}{\partial \theta} + \frac{\partial v_z}{\partial z} = 0$$

EQUATION OF MOTION

Equation of Motion (in terms of $\underline{\underline{\tau}}$)

$$\rho\frac{D\underline{v}}{Dt} = -\nabla p + [\nabla \cdot \underline{\underline{\tau}}] + \rho\underline{g}$$

Rectangular coordinates (x,y,z)

$$\rho\left(\frac{\partial v_x}{\partial t} + v_x\frac{\partial v_x}{\partial x} + v_y\frac{\partial v_x}{\partial y} + v_z\frac{\partial v_x}{\partial z}\right) = -\frac{\partial p}{\partial x} + \left(\frac{\partial \tau_{xx}}{\partial x} + \frac{\partial \tau_{yx}}{\partial y} + \frac{\partial \tau_{zx}}{\partial z}\right) + \rho g_x$$

$$\rho\left(\frac{\partial v_y}{\partial t} + v_x\frac{\partial v_y}{\partial x} + v_y\frac{\partial v_y}{\partial y} + v_z\frac{\partial v_y}{\partial z}\right) = -\frac{\partial p}{\partial y} + \left(\frac{\partial \tau_{xy}}{\partial x} + \frac{\partial \tau_{yy}}{\partial y} + \frac{\partial \tau_{zy}}{\partial z}\right) + \rho g_y$$

$$\rho\left(\frac{\partial v_z}{\partial t} + v_x\frac{\partial v_z}{\partial x} + v_y\frac{\partial v_z}{\partial y} + v_z\frac{\partial v_z}{\partial z}\right) = -\frac{\partial p}{\partial z} + \left(\frac{\partial \tau_{xz}}{\partial x} + \frac{\partial \tau_{yz}}{\partial y} + \frac{\partial \tau_{zz}}{\partial z}\right) + \rho g_z$$

Cylindrical coordinates (r,θ,z)

$$\rho\left(\frac{\partial v_r}{\partial t} + v_r\frac{\partial v_r}{\partial r} + \frac{v_\theta}{r}\frac{\partial v_r}{\partial \theta} - \frac{v_\theta^2}{r} + v_z\frac{\partial v_r}{\partial z}\right) = -\frac{\partial p}{\partial r} + \left(\frac{1}{r}\frac{\partial}{\partial x}(r\tau_{rr}) + \frac{1}{r}\frac{\partial \tau_{r\theta}}{\partial \theta} - \frac{\tau_{\theta\theta}}{r} + \frac{\partial \tau_{rz}}{\partial z}\right) + \rho g_r$$

$$\rho\left(\frac{\partial v_\theta}{\partial t} + v_r\frac{\partial v_\theta}{\partial r} + \frac{v_\theta}{r}\frac{\partial v_\theta}{\partial \theta} + \frac{v_r v_\theta}{r} + v_z\frac{\partial v_\theta}{\partial z}\right) = -\frac{1}{r}\frac{\partial p}{\partial \theta} + \left(\frac{1}{r^2}\frac{\partial}{\partial r}(r^2\tau_{r\theta}) + \frac{1}{r}\frac{\partial \tau_{\theta\theta}}{\partial \theta} + \frac{\partial \tau_{\theta z}}{\partial z}\right) + \rho g_\theta$$

$$\rho\left(\frac{\partial v_z}{\partial t} + v_r\frac{\partial v_z}{\partial r} + \frac{v_\theta}{r}\frac{\partial v_z}{\partial \theta} + v_z\frac{\partial v_z}{\partial z}\right) = -\frac{\partial p}{\partial z} + \left(\frac{1}{r}\frac{\partial}{\partial r}(r\tau_{rz}) + \frac{1}{r}\frac{\partial \tau_{\theta z}}{\partial \theta} + \frac{\partial \tau_{zz}}{\partial z}\right) + \rho g_z$$

Equation of Motion (in terms of $\underline{v}$) **(Navier-Stokes Equations)**

$$\rho\frac{D\underline{v}}{Dt} = -\nabla p + \mu\nabla^2\underline{v} + \rho\underline{g}$$

Rectangular coordinates (x,y,z)

$$\rho\left(\frac{\partial v_x}{\partial t} + v_x\frac{\partial v_x}{\partial x} + v_y\frac{\partial v_x}{\partial y} + v_z\frac{\partial v_x}{\partial z}\right) = -\frac{\partial p}{\partial x} + \mu\left(\frac{\partial^2 v_x}{\partial x^2} + \frac{\partial^2 v_x}{\partial y^2} + \frac{\partial^2 v_x}{\partial z^2}\right) + \rho g_x$$

$$\rho\left(\frac{\partial v_y}{\partial t} + v_x\frac{\partial v_y}{\partial x} + v_y\frac{\partial v_y}{\partial y} + v_z\frac{\partial v_y}{\partial z}\right) = -\frac{\partial p}{\partial y} + \mu\left(\frac{\partial^2 v_y}{\partial x^2} + \frac{\partial^2 v_y}{\partial y^2} + \frac{\partial^2 v_y}{\partial z^2}\right) + \rho g_y$$

$$\rho\left(\frac{\partial v_z}{\partial t} + v_x\frac{\partial v_z}{\partial x} + v_y\frac{\partial v_z}{\partial y} + v_z\frac{\partial v_z}{\partial z}\right) = -\frac{\partial p}{\partial z} + \mu\left(\frac{\partial^2 v_z}{\partial x^2} + \frac{\partial^2 v_z}{\partial y^2} + \frac{\partial^2 v_z}{\partial z^2}\right) + \rho g_z$$

Cylindrical coordinates (r,θ,z)

$$\rho\left(\frac{\partial v_r}{\partial t} + v_r\frac{\partial v_r}{\partial r} + \frac{v_\theta}{r}\frac{\partial v_r}{\partial \theta} - \frac{v_\theta^2}{r} + v_z\frac{\partial v_r}{\partial z}\right) =$$

$$-\frac{\partial p}{\partial r} + \mu\left(\frac{\partial}{\partial r}\left(\frac{1}{r}\frac{\partial}{\partial r}(rv_r)\right) + \frac{1}{r^2}\frac{\partial^2 v_r}{\partial \theta^2} - \frac{2}{r^2}\frac{\partial v_\theta}{\partial \theta} + \frac{\partial^2 v_r}{\partial z^2}\right) + \rho g_r$$

$$\rho\left(\frac{\partial v_\theta}{\partial t} + v_r\frac{\partial v_\theta}{\partial r} + \frac{v_\theta}{r}\frac{\partial v_\theta}{\partial \theta} + \frac{v_r v_\theta}{r} + v_z\frac{\partial v_\theta}{\partial z}\right) =$$

$$-\frac{1}{r}\frac{\partial p}{\partial \theta} + \mu\left(\frac{\partial}{\partial r}\left(\frac{1}{r}\frac{\partial}{\partial r}(rv_\theta)\right) + \frac{1}{r^2}\frac{\partial^2 v_\theta}{\partial \theta^2} - \frac{2}{r^2}\frac{\partial v_r}{\partial \theta} + \frac{\partial^2 v_\theta}{\partial z^2}\right) + \rho g_\theta$$

$$\rho\left(\frac{\partial v_z}{\partial t} + v_r\frac{\partial v_z}{\partial r} + \frac{v_\theta}{r}\frac{\partial v_z}{\partial \theta} + v_z\frac{\partial v_z}{\partial z}\right) =$$

$$-\frac{\partial p}{\partial z} + \mu\left(\frac{1}{r}\frac{\partial}{\partial r}\left(r\frac{\partial v_z}{\partial r}\right) + \frac{1}{r^2}\frac{\partial^2 v_z}{\partial \theta^2} + \frac{\partial^2 v_z}{\partial z^2}\right) + \rho g_z$$

A7 Properties Tables

Table I Guide Values of the Physical Properties of Plastics

Polymer	Abbre-viation	Density		Mechanical properties	
		g/cm^3	lb/in^3	Tensile strength	
				N/mm^2	psi
Low density polyethylene	PE-LD	0.914/0.928	0.0329–0.0330	8/23	1140/3270
High density polyethylene	PE-HD	0.94/0.96	0.0338–0.0345	18/35	2560/4980
EVA	EVA	0.92/0.95	0.0331–0.0341	10/20	1420/2840
Polypropylene	PP	0.90/0.907	0.0324–0.0327	21/37	2990/5260
Polybutene-1	PB	0.905/0.920	0.0325–0.0331	30/38	4270/5400
Polyisobutylene	PIB	0.91/0.93	0.0327–0.0334	2/6	284/853
Poly-4-methylpent-1-ene	PMP	0.83	0.0298	25/28	3560/3980
Ionomers	–	0.94	0.0338	21/35	2990/4980
Rigid PVC	PVC-U	1.38/1.55	0.0496–0.0557	50/75	7110/10670
Plasticized PVC	PVC-P	1.16/1.35	0.0417–0.0486	10/25	1420/3560
Polystyrene	PS	1.05	0.0378	45/65	6400/9240
Styrene/acrylonitrile copolymer	SAN	1.08	0.0392	75	10670
Styrene/polybutadiene graft polymer	SB	1.05	0.0378	26/38	3700/5400
Acrylonitrile/polybut./styrene graft polymer	ABS	1.04/1.06	0.0374–0.0381	32/45	4550/6400
AN/AN elastomers/styrene graft polymer	ASA	1.04	0.0374	32	4550
Polymethylmethacrylate	PMMA	1.17/1.20	0.0421–0.0431	50/77	7110/10950
Polyvinylcarbazole	PVK	1.19	0.0428	20/30	2840/4270
Polyacetal	POM	1.41/1.42	0.0507–0.0511	62/70	8820/9960
Polytetrafluoroethylene	PTFE	2.15/2.20	0.0774–0.0791	25/36	3560/5120
Tetrafluoroethylene/hexafluoropropylene copolymer	FEP	2.12/2.17	0.0763–0.0781	22/28	3130/3980
Polytrifluorochlorethylene	PCTFE	2.10/2.12	0.0755–0.0762	32/40	4550/5690
Ethylene/tetrafluoroethylene	E/TFE	1.7	0.0611	35/54	4980/7680
Polyamide 6	PA 6	1.13	0.0406	70/85	9960/12090
Polyamide 66	PA 66	1.14	0.0410	77/84	10950/11950
Polyamide 11	PA 11	1.04	0.0374	56	7960
Polyamide 12	PA 12	1.02	0.0367	56/65	7960/9240
Polyamide 6-3-T	PA-6-3-T	1.12	0.0403	70/84	9960/11950
Polycarbonate	PC	1.2	0.0432	56/67	7960/9530
Polyethyleneterephthalate	PET	1.37	0.0492	47	6680
Polybutyleneterephthalate	PBT	1.31	0.0471	40	5690
Polyphenyleneether modified	PPE	1.06	0.0381	55/68	7820/9670
Polysulfone	PSU	1.24	0.0446	50/100	7110/14200
Polyphenylenesulfide	PPS	1.34	0.0483	75	10670
Polyarylsulfone	PAS	1.36	0.0490	90	12800
Polyethersulfone	PES	1.37	0.0492	85	12090
Polyarylether	PAE	1.14	0.0411	53	7540
Phenol/formaldehyde, grade 31	PF	1.4	0.0504	25	3560
Urea/formaldehyde, grade 131	UF	1.5	0.0540	30	4270
Melamine/formaldehyde, grade 152	MF	1.5	0.0540	30	4270
Unsaturated polyester resin, grade 802	UP	2.0	0.0720	30	4270
Polydiallylphthalate (GF) molding compound	PDAP	1.51/1.78	0.0543–0.0640	40/75	5690/10670
Silicone resin molding compound	SI	1.8/1.9	0.0648–0.0684	28/46	3980/6540
Polyimide molding	PI	1.43	0.0515	75/100	10570/14200
Epoxy resin, grade 891	EP	1.9	0.0683	30/40	4270/5690
Polyurethane casting resin	PU	1.05	0.0378	70/80	9960/11380
Thermoplastic PU-elastomers	PU	1.20	0.0432	30/40	4270/5690
Linear polyurethane (U$_{50}$)	PU	1.21	0.0435	30 (σ_s)	4270 (σ_y)
Vulcanized fiber	VF	1.1/1.45	0.0396–0.0522	85/100	12090/14200
Celluloseacetate, grade 432	CA	1.30	0.0468	38 (σ_s)	5400 (σ_s)
Cellulosepropionate	CP	1.19/1.23	0.0429–0.0452	14/55	7990/7820
Celluloseacetobutyrate, grade 413	CAB	1.18	0.0425	26 (σ_s)	3600 (σ_y)

Elongation at break %	Tensile modulus of elasticity		Ball indentation hardness		Impact strength kJ/m²	Notched impact strength	
	N/mm²	kpsi	10-s-value	10-s-value psi		kJ/m²	ft lb/ in of notch
00/1000	200/500	28.4/71.1	13/20	1850/2840	no break	no break	–
00/1000	700/1400	99.6/199	40/65	5690/9240	no break	no break	–
00/900	7/120	0.99/17.1	–	–	no break	no break	no break
0/800	11000/1300	156/185	36/70	5120/9960	no break	3/17	0.5/20
50/280	250/350	35.6/49.8	30/38	4270/5400	no break	4/no break	no break
> 1000	–	–	–	–	no break	no break	no break
3/22	1100/1500	156/213	–	–	–	–	0.4/0.6
50/500	180/210	25.6/29.9	–	–	–	–	6/15
0/50	1000/3500	142/498	75/155	10670/22000	no break/ > 20	2/50	0.4/20
70/400	–	–	–	–	no break	no break	–
/4	3200/3250	455/462	120/130	17100/18500	5/20	2/2.5	0.25/0.6
	3600	512	130/140	18500/19900	8/20	2/3	0.35/0.5
5/60	1800/2500	256/356	80/130	11380/18500	10/80	5/13	no break
5/30	1900/2700	270/384	80/120	11380/17100	70/no break	7/20	2.5/12
0	1800	256	75	10670	no break	18	6/8
/10	2700/3200	384/455	180/200	25600/28400	18	2	0.3/0.5
	3500	498	200	28400	5	2	–
5/70	2800/3200	398/455	150/170	21300/24200	100	8	1/2.3
50/550	410	58.3	27/35	3840/4980	no break	13/15	3.0
50/330	350	49.8	30/32	4270/4550	–	–	no break
20/175	1050/2100	149/299	65/70	9240/9960	no break	8/10	2.5/2.8
00/500	1100	156	65	9240	–	–	no break
00/300	1400	199	75	10670	no break	no break	3.0
50/300	2000	284	100	14200	no break	15/20	2.1
00	1000	142	75	10670	no break	30/40	1.8
00	1600	228	75	10670	no break	10/20	2/5.5
0/150	2000	284	160	22800	no break	13	–
00/130	2100/2400	299/341	110	15600	no break	20/30	12/18
0/300	3100	441	200	28400	no break	4	0.8/1.0
5	2000	284	180	25600	no break	4	0.8/1.0
0/60	2500	356	–	–	no break	–	4
5/30	2600/2750	370/391	–	–	–	–	1.3
3	3400	484	–	–	–	–	0.3
0/80	2600	370	–	–	–	–	1/2
5/90	2450	348	–	–	–	–	1.6
	2250	320	–	–	–	–	8.0
4/0.8	5600/12000	796/1710	250/320	35600/45500	> 6	> 1.5	0.2/0.6
5/1.0	7000/10500	996/1490	260/350	39000/49800	> 6.5	> 2.5	0.5/0.4
6/0.9	4900/9100	697/1294	260/410	37000/58300	> 7.0	> 1.5	0.2/0.3
6/1.2	14000/20000	1990/2840	240	34100	> 4.5	> 3.0	0.5/16
	9800/15500	1394/2200	–	–	–	–	0.4/15
	6000/12000	853/1710	–	–	–	–	0.3/0.8
/9	23000/28000	3270/3980	–	–	–	–	0.5/1.0
/6	21500	3060	–	–	> 8	> 3	2/30
	4000	569	–	–	–	–	0.4
00/450	700	99.6	–	–	no break	no break	no break
5 (ε_s)	1000	140	–	–	no break	3	–
	–	–	80/140	11380/19900	20/120	–	–
(ε_s)	2200	313	50	7110	65	15	2.5
0/100	420/1500	59,7/213	47/79	6680/11240	no break	6/20	1.5
(ε_s)	1600	228	35/43	4980/6120	no break	30/35	4/5

(continued on next page)

Table I *(cont.)* Guide Values of the Physical Properties of Plastics

Polymer	Abbre-viation	Density	
		g/cm^3	lb/in^3
Low density polyethylene	PE-LD	0.914/0.928	0.0329–0.0330
High density polyethylene	PE-HD	0.94/0.96	0.0338–0.0345
EVA	EVA	0.92/0.95	0.0331–0.0341
Polypropylene	PP	0.90/0.907	0.0324–0.0327
Polybutene-1	PB	0.905/0.920	0.0325–0.0331
Polyisobutylene	PIB	0.91/0.93	0.0327–0.0334
Poly-4-methylpent-1-ene	PMP	0.83	0.0298
Ionomers	–	0.94	0.0338
Rigid PVC	PVC-U	1.38/1.55	0.0496–0.0557
Plasticized PVC	PVC-P	1.16/1.35	0.0417–0.0486
Polystyrene	PS	1.05	0.0378
Styrene/acrylonitrile copolymer	SAN	1.08	0.0392
Styrene/polybutadiene graft polymer	SB	1.05	0.0378
Acrylonitrile/polybut./styrene graft polymer	ABS	1.04/1.06	0.0374–0.0381
AN/AN elastomers/styrene graft polymer	ASA	1.04	0.0374
Polymethylmethacrylate	PMMA	1.17/1.20	0.0421–0.0431
Polyvinylcarbazole	PVK	1.19	0.0428
Polyacetal	POM	1.41/1.42	0.0507–0.0511
Polytetrafluoroethylene	PTFE	2.15/2.20	0.0774–0.0791
Tetrafluoroethylene/hexafluoropropylene copolymer	FEP	2.12/2.17	0.0763–0.0781
Polytrifluorochlorethylene	PCTFE	2.10/2.12	0.0755–0.0762
Ethylene/tetrafluoroethylene	E/TFE	1.7	0.0611
Polyamide 6	PA 6	1.13	0.0406
Polyamide 66	PA 66	1.14	0.0410
Polyamide 11	PA 11	1.04	0.0374
Polyamide 12	PA 12	1.02	0.0367
Polyamide 6-3-T	PA-6-3-T	1.12	0.0403
Polycarbonate	PC	1.2	0.0432
Polyethyleneterephthalate	PET	1.37	0.0492
Polybutyleneterephthalate	PBT	1.31	0.0471
Polyphenyleneether modified	PPE	1.06	0.0381
Polysulfone	PSU	1.24	0.0446
Polyphenylenesulfide	PPS	1.34	0.0483
Polyarylsulfone	PAS	1.36	0.0490
Polyethersulfone	PES	1.37	0.0492
Polyarylether	PAE	1.14	0.0411
Phenol/formaldehyde, grade 31	PF	1.4	0.0504
Urea/formaldehyde, grade 131	UF	1.5	0.0540
Melamine/formaldehyde, grade 152	MF	1.5	0.0540
Unsaturated polyester resin, grade 802	UP	2.0	0.0720
Polydiallylphthalate (GF) molding compound	PDAP	1.51/1.78	0.0543–0.0640
Silicone resin molding compound	SI	1.8/1.9	0.0648–0.0684
Polyimide molding	PI	1.43	0.0515
Epoxy resin, grade 891	EP	1.9	0.0683
Polyurethane casting resin	PU	1.05	0.0378
Thermoplastic PU-elastomers	PU	1.20	0.0432
Linear polyurethane (U$_{50}$)	PU	1.21	0.0435
Vulcanized fiber	VF	1.1/1.45	0.0396–0.0522
Celluloseacetate, grade 432	CA	1.30	0.0468
Cellulosepropionate	CP	1.19/1.23	0.0429–0.0452
Celluloseacetobutyrate, grade 413	CAB	1.18	0.0425

Optical properties		Water absorption	
Refractive index n_D^{20}	Transparency	mg (4 d)	% (24 h)
1.51	transparent	<0.01	<0.01
1.53	opaque	<0.01	<0.01
–	transparent/opaque	–	0.05/0.13
1.49	transparent/opaque	<0.01	0.01/0.03
–	opaque	<0.01	<0.02
–	opaque	<0.01	<0.01
1.46	opaque	–	0.01
1.51	transparent	–	0.1/1.4
1.52/1.55	transparent/opaque	3/18	0.04/0.4
–	transparent/opaque	6/30	0.15/0.75
1.59	transparent	–	0.03/0.1
1.57	transparent	–	0.2/0.3
–	opaque	–	0.05/0.6
–	opaque	–	0.2/0.45
–	translucent/opaque	–	–
1.49	transparent	35/45	0.1/0.4
–	opaque	0.5	0.1/0.2
1.48	opaque	20/30	0.22/0.25
1.35	opaque	–	0
1.34	transparent/translucent	–	<0.1
1.43	translucent/opaque	–	0
1.40	transparent/opaque	–	0.03
1.53	translucent/opaque	–	1.3/1.9
1.53	translucent/opaque	–	1.5
1.52	translucent/opaque	–	0.3
–	translucent/opaque	–	0.25
1.53	transparent	–	0.4
1.58	transparent	10	0.16
–	transparent/opaque	18/20	0.30
–	opaque	–	0.08
–	opaque	–	0.06
1.63	transparent/opaque	–	0.02
–	opaque	–	0.02
1.67	opaque	–	1.8
1.65	transparent	–	0.43
–	translucent/opaque	–	0.25
–	opaque	<150	0.3/1.2
–	opaque	<300	0.4/0.8
–	opaque	<250	0.1/0.6
–	opaque	<45	0.03/0.5
–	opaque	–	0.12/0.35
–	opaque	–	0.2
–	opaque	–	0.32
–	opaque	<30	0.05/0.2
–	transparent	–	0.1/0.2
–	translucent/opaque	–	0.7/0.9
–	translucent/opaque	130	–
–	opaque	–	7/9
1.50	transparent	130	6
1.47	transparent	40/60	1.2/2.8
1.47	transparent	40/60	0.9/3.2

(continued on next page)

Table I *(cont.)* Guide Values of the Physical Properties of Plastics

Polymer	Abbreviation	Density		Thermal properties			
				Service temperature			
				max./short time		max./continuous	
		g/cm³	lb/in³	°C	°F	°C	°F
Low density polyethylene	PE-LD	0.914/0.928	0.0329–0.0330	80/90	176/194	60/75	140/16
High density polyethylene	PE-HD	0.94/0.96	0.0338–0.0345	90/120	194/248	70/80	158/17
EVA	EVA	0.92/0.95	0.0331–0.0341	65	149	55	131
Polypropylene	PP	0.90/0.907	0.0324–0.0327	140	284	100	212
Polybutene-1	PB	0.905/0.920	0.0325–0.0331	130	266	90	194
Polyisobutylene	PIB	0.91/0.93	0.0327–0.0334	80	176	65	149
Poly-4-methylpent-1-ene	PMP	0.83	0.0298	180	356	120	248
Ionomers	–	0.94	0.0338	120	248	100	212
Rigid PVC	PVC-U	1.38/1.55	0.0496–0.0557	75/100	167/212	65/85	149/15
Plasticized PVC	PVC-P	1.16/1.35	0.0417–0.0486	55/65	131/149	50/55	122/13
Polystyrene	PS	1.05	0.0378	60/80	140/176	50/70	122/15
Styrene/acrylonitrile copolymer	SAN	1.08	0.0392	95	203	85	185
Styrene/polybutadiene graft	SB	1.05	0.0378	60/80	140/176	50/70	122/15
Acrylonitrile/polybut./ styrene graft polymer	ABS	1.04/1.06	0.0374–0.0381	85/100	188/212	75/85	167/18
AN/AN elastomers/ styrene graft polymer	ASA	1.04	0.0374	85/90	188/194	70/75	158/16
Polymethylmethacrylate	PMMA	1.17/1.20	0.0421–0.0431	85/100	188/212	65/90	149/19
Polyvinylcarbazole	PVK	1.19	0.0428	170	338	160	320
Polyacetal	POM	1.41/1.42	0.0507–0.0511	110/140	230	90/110	194/23
Polytetrafluoroethylene	PTFE	2.15/2.20	0.0774–0.0791	300	572	250	482
Tetrafluoroethylene hexafluoropropylene copolymer	FEP	2.12/2.17	0.0763–0.0781	250	482	205	401
Polytrifluorochlorethylene	PCTFE	2.10/2.12	0.0755–0.0762	180	356	150	302
Ethylene tetrafluoroethylene	E/TFE	1.7	0.0611	220	428	150	302
Polyamide 6	PA 6	1.13	0.0406	140/180	284/356	80/100	176/21
Polyamide 66	PA 66	1.14	0.0410	170/200	338/392	80/120	176/24
Polyamide 11	PA 11	1.04	0.0374	140/150	284/302	70/80	158/17
Polyamide 12	PA 12	1.02	0.0367	140/150	284/302	70/80	158/17
Polyamide 6-3-T	PA-6-3-T	1.12	0.0403	130/140	266/284	80/100	176/21
Polycarbonate	PC	1.2	0.0432	160	320	135	275
Polyethyleneterephthalate	PET	1.37	0.0492	200	392	100	212
Polybutyleneterephthalate	PBT	1.31	0.0471	165	329	100	212
Polyphenyleneether modified	PPE	1.06	0.0381	150	302	80	176
Polysulfone	PSU	1.24	0.0446	200	392	150	302
Polyphenylensulfide	PPS	1.34	0.0483	300	572	200	392
Polyarylsulfone	PAS	1.36	0.0490	300	572	260	500
Polyethersulfone	PES	1.37	0.0492	260	500	200	392
Polyarylether	PAE	1.14	0.0411	160	320	120	248
Phenol/formaldehyde, grade 31	PF	1.4	0.0504	140	284	110	230
Urea/formaldehyde, grade 131	UF	1.5	0.0540	100	212	70	158
Melamine/formaldehyde, grade 152	MF	1.5	0.0540	120	248	80	176
Unsaturated polyester resin, grade 802	UP	2.0	0.0720	200	392	150	302
Polydiallylphthalate (GF) molding compound	PDAP	1.51/1.78	0.0543–0.0640	190/250	374/482	150/180	302/3
Silicone resin molding compound	SI	1.8/1.9	0.0648–0.0684	250	482	170/180	338/3
Polyimide molding	PI	1.43	0.0515	400	752	260	500
Epoxy resin, grade 891	EP	1.9	0.0683	180	356	130	266
Polyurethane casting resin	PU	1.05	0.0378	100	212	80	176
Thermoplastic PU-elastomers	PU	1.20	0.0432	110	230	80	176
Linear polyurethane (U₅₀)	PU	1.21	0.0435	80	176	60	140
Vulcanized fiber	VF	1.1/1.45	0.0396–0.0522	180	356	105	221
Celluloseacetate, grade 432	CA	1.30	0.0468	80	176	70	158
Cellulosepropionate	CP	1.19/1.23	0.0429–0.0452	80/120	176/248	60/115	140/2
Celluloseacetobutyrate, grade 413	CAB	1.18	0.0425	80/120	176/248	60/115	140/2

		Heat deflection temperature				Coefficient of linear expansion		Thermal conductivity		Specific heat	
in./continuous		°C		°F		$K^{-1}\cdot10^6$	in/in/°F 10^{-6}	W/mK	BTU in/ ft²h°F	kJ/ kgK	BTU/ lb°F
°C	°F	VSP (Vicat 5 kg)	1.86/ 0.45 N/ mm²	VSP (Vicat lb)	264/ 66 psi						
-50	-58	–	35	–	95	250	140	0.32/0.40	2.2/2.8	2.1/2.5	8.8/10.5
-50	-58	60/70	50	140/158	122	200	110	0.38/0.51	2.6/3.5	2.1/2.7	8.8/11.5
-60	-76	–	34/62	–	93/144	160/200	90/110	0.35	2.4	2.3	9.5
-30	32/-22	85/100	45/120	185/212	113/248	150	83	0.17/0.22	1.2/1.5	2.0	8.3
	32	70	60/110	158	140/230	150	83	0.20	1.4	1.8	7.5
-50	-58	–	–	–	–	120	67	0.12/0.20	0.8/1.4	–	–
	32	–	–	–	–	117	65	0.17	1.2	2.18	9.1
-50	-58	–	38/45	–	100/113	120	67	0.24	1.7	2.20	9.2
-5	21	75/110	60/82	167/230	140/180	70/80	39/45	0.14/0.17	1.0/1.2	0.85/0.9	3.55/3.75
-20	32/-4	40	–	104	–	150/210	83/110	0.15	1.05	0.9/1.8	3.75/7.5
-10	14	78/99	110/80	172/210	230/176	70	39	0.18	1.25	1.3	5.4
-20	-4	–	104/90	–	219/194	80	45	0.18	1.25	1.3	5.4
-20	-4	77/95	104/82	171/203	219/180	70	39	0.18	1.25	1.3	5.4
-40	-40	95/110	80/120	203/230	176/248	60/110	33/61	0.18	1.25	1.3	5.4
-40	-40	92	100/110	198	212/230	80/110	44/61	0.18	1.25	1.3	5.4
-40	-40	70/100	60/100	158/212	140/212	70	39	0.18	1.25	1.47	6.15
-100	-148	180	–	356	–	–	–	0.29	2.0	–	–
-60	-76	160/173	110/170	320/344	230/338	90/110	50/61	0.25/0.30	1.7/2.1	1.46	6.1
-200	-328	–	–/121	–	–/250	100	56	0.25	1.7	1.0	4.20
-100	-148	–	–/70	–	–/158	80	45	0.25	1.7	1.12	4.65
-40	-40	–	–/126	–	–/259	60	33	0.22	1.5	0.9	3.75
-190	-310	–	71/104	–	160/219	40	22	0.23	1.6	0.9	3.75
-30	-22	180	80/190	356	176/374	80	44	0.29	2.0	1.7	7.1
-30	-22	200	105/200	392	221/392	80	44	0.23	1.6	1.7	7.1
-70	-94	175	150/130	347	302/266	130	72	0.23	1.6	1.26	5.25
-70	-94	165	140/150	329	284/302	150	83	0.23	1.6	1.26	5.25
-70	-94	145	140/80	293	284/176	80	45	0.23	1.6	1.6	6.70
-100	-148	138	130/145	280	266/293	60/70	33/39	0.21	1.45	1.17	4.90
-20	-4	188	–	280	–	70	39	0.24	1.65	1.05	4.40
-30	-22	178	50/190	352	122/374	60	33	0.21	1.45	1.30	5.40
-30	-22	148	100/140	298	212/284	60	33	0.23	1.60	1.40	5.85
-100	-148	–	175/180	–	347/356	54	30	0.28	1.95	1.30	5.40
		–	137/–	–	277/–	55	31	0.25	1.70	–	–
		–	–	–	–	47	26	0.16	1.10	–	–
		–	–	–	–	55	31	0.18	1.25	1.10	4.6
		–	150/160	–	302/320	65	36	0.26	1.80	1.46	6.1
		–	150/190	–	302/374	30/50	17/28	0.35	2.40	1.30	5.40
		–	130/–	–	266/–	50/60	28/33	0.40	2.75	1.20	5.0
		–	180/–	–	356/–	50/60	28/33	0.50	3.45	1.20	5.0
		–	230/–	–	446/–	20/40	11/22	0.70	4.85	1.20	5.0
-50	-58	–	220/–	–	428/–	10/35	55/19	0.60	4.15	–	5.0
-50	-58	–	480/–	–	896/–	20/50	11/28	0.3/0.4	2.05/2.75	0.8/0.9	3.35/3.75
-200	-239	–	240/–	–	464/–	50/63	28/35	0.6/0.65	4.15/4.50	–	–
		–	200/–	–	392/–	11/35	6.1/19	0.88	6.1	0.8	3.35
		–	90/–	–	194/–	10/20	5.5/11	0.58	4.0	1.76	7.30
-40	-40	–	–	–	–	150	83	1.7	1.15	0.5	2.10
-15	3	100	–	212	–	210	12	1.8	1.25	0.4	1.65
-30	-22	–	–	–	–	–	–	–	–	–	–
-40	-40	50/63	90/–	122/144	194/–	120	67	0.22	1.50	1.6	6.7
-40	-40	100	73/98	212	163/208	110/130	61/72	0.21	1.45	1.7	7.1
-40	-40	60/75	62/71	140/167	144/160	120	67	0.21	1.45	1.6	6.7

(continued on next page)

Table I *(cont.)* Guide Values of the Physical Properties of Plastics

Polymer	DIN 7728 Bl. 1	Density		Electrical properties	
		g/cm³	lb/in³	Volume resistivity Ω cm	Surface resistance Ω
Low density polyethylene	PE-LD	0.914/0.928	0.0329–0.0330	$>10^{17}$	10^{14}
High density polyethylene	PE-HD	0.94/0.96	0.0338–0.0345	$>10^{17}$	10^{14}
EVA	EVA	0.92/0.95	0.0331–0.0341	$<10^{15}$	10^{13}
Polypropylene	PP	0.90/0.907	0.0324–0.0327	$>10^{17}$	10^{13}
Polybutene-1	PB	0.905/0.920	0.0325–0.0331	$>10^{17}$	10^{13}
Polyisobutylene	PIB	0.91/0.93	0.0327–0.0334	$>10^{15}$	10^{13}
Poly-4-methylpent-1-ene	PMP	0.83	0.0298	$>10^{16}$	10^{13}
Ionomers	–	0.94	0.0338	$>10^{16}$	10^{13}
Rigid PVC	PVC-U	1.38/1.55	0.0496–0.0557	$>10^{15}$	10^{13}
Plasticized PVC	PVC-P	1.16/1.35	0.0417–0.0486	$>10^{11}$	10^{11}
Polystyrene	PS	1.05	0.0378	$>10^{16}$	$>10^{13}$
Styrene/acrylonitrile copolymer	SAN	1.08	0.0392	$>10^{16}$	$>10^{13}$
Styrene/polybutadiene graft polymer	SB	1.05	0.0378	$>10^{16}$	$>10^{13}$
Acrylonitrile/polybut./styrene graft polymer	ABS	1.04/1.06	0.0374–0.0381	$>10^{15}$	$>10^{13}$
AN/AN elastomers/styrene graft polymer	ASA	1.04	0.0374	$>10^{15}$	$>10^{13}$
Polymethylmethacrylate	PMMA	1.17/1.20	0.0421–0.0431	$>10^{15}$	10^{15}
Polyvinylcarbazole	PVK	1.19	0.0428	$>10^{16}$	10^{14}
Polyacetal	POM	1.41/1.42	0.0507–0.0511	$>10^{15}$	10^{13}
Polytetrafluoroethylene	PTFE	2.15/2.20	0.0774–0.0791	$>10^{18}$	10^{17}
Tetrafluoroethylene/hexafluoropropylene copolymer	FEP	2.12/2.17	0.0763–0.0781	$>10^{18}$	10^{16}
Polytrifluorochloroethylene	PCTFE	2.10/2.12	0.0755–0.0762	$>10^{18}$	10^{16}
Ethylene/tetrafluoroethylene	E/TFE	1.7	0.0611	$>10^{16}$	10^{13}
Polyamide 6	PA 6	1.13	0.0406	10^{12}	10^{10}
Polyamide 66	PA 66	1.14	0.0410	10^{12}	10^{10}
Polyamide 11	PA 11	1.04	0.0374	10^{13}	10^{11}
Polyamide 12	PA 12	1.02	0.0367	10^{13}	10^{11}
Polyamide 6-3-T	PA-6-3-T	1.12	0.0403	10^{11}	10^{10}
Polycarbonate	PC	1.2	0.0432	$>10^{17}$	$>10^{15}$
Polyethyleneterephthalate	PET	1.37	0.0492	10^{16}	10^{16}
Polybutyleneterephthalate	PBT	1.31	0.0471	10^{16}	10^{13}
Polyphenyleneether modified	PPE	1.06	0.0381	10^{16}	10^{14}
Polysulfone	PSU	1.24	0.0446	$>10^{16}$	–
Polyphenylenesulfide	PPS	1.34	0.0483	$>10^{16}$	–
Polyarylsulfone	PAS	1.36	0.0490	$>10^{16}$	–
Polyethersulfone	PES	1.37	0.0492	10^{17}	–
Polyarylether	PAE	1.14	0.0411	$>10^{10}$	–
Phenol/formaldehyde, grade 31	PF	1.4	0.0504	10^{11}	$>10^{8}$
Urea/formaldehyde, grade 131	UF	1.5	0.0540	10^{11}	$>10^{10}$
Melamine/formaldehyde, grade 152	MF	1.5	0.0540	11^{11}	$>10^{8}$
Unsaturated polyester resin, grade 802	UP	2.0	0.0720	$>10^{12}$	$>10^{10}$
Polydiallylphthalate (GF) molding compound	PDAP	1.51/1.78	0.0543–0.0640	$10^{13}/10^{16}$	10^{13}
Silicone resin molding compound	SI	1.8/1.9	0.0648–0.0684	10^{14}	10^{12}
Polyimide molding	PI	1.43	0.0515	$>10^{16}$	$>10^{15}$
Epoxy resin, grade 891	EP	1.9	0.0683	$>10^{14}$	$>10^{12}$
Polyurethane casting resin	PU	1.05	0.0378	10^{16}	10^{14}
Thermoplastic PU-elastomers	PU	1.20	0.0432	10^{12}	10^{11}
Linear polyurethane (U$_{50}$)	PU	1.21	0.0435	10^{13}	10^{12}
Vulcanized fiber	VF	1.1/1.45	0.0396–0.0522	10^{10}	10^{8}
Celluloseacetate, grade 432	CA	1.30	0.0468	10^{13}	10^{12}
Cellulosepropionate	CP	1.19/1.23	0.0429–0.0452	10^{16}	10^{14}
Celluloseacetobutyrate, grade 413	CAB	1.18	0.0425	10^{16}	10^{14}

Dielectric constant		Dissipation (power) factor tan δ		Dielectric strength		Tracking resistance		
0 Hz	10^6 Hz	50 Hz	10^6 Hz	kV/25 μm	kV/cm	KA	KB	KC
29	2.28	$1.5 \cdot 10^4$	$0.8 \cdot 10^{-4}$	>700	–	3b	>600	>600
35	2.34	$2.4 \cdot 10^{-4}$	$2.0 \cdot 10^{-4}$	>700	–	3c	>600	>600
5/3.2	2.6/3.2	0.003/0.02	0.03/0.05	–	620/780	–	–	–
27	2.25	$<4 \cdot 10^{-4}$	$<5 \cdot 10^{-4}$	800	500/650	3c	>600	>600
5	2.2	$7 \cdot 10^{-4}$	$6 \cdot 10^{-4}$	700	–	3c	>600	>600
3	–	0.0004	–	230	–	3c	>600	>600
12	2.12	$7 \cdot 10^{-5}$	$3 \cdot 10^{-5}$	280	700	3c	>600	>600
5	3.0	0.011	0.015	200/400	350/500	2/3b	600	600
8	4/4.5	0.08	0.12	150/300	300/400	–	–	–
5	2.5	$1/4 \cdot 10^{-4}$	$0.5/4 \cdot 10^{-4}$	500	300/700	1/2	140	150/250
6/3.4	2.6/3.1	$6/8 \cdot 10^{-3}$	$7/10 \cdot 10^{-3}$	500	400/500	1/2	160	150/260
4/4.7	2.4/3.8	$4/20 \cdot 10^{-4}$	$4/20 \cdot 10^{-4}$	500	300/600	2	>600	>600
4/5	2.4/3.8	$3/8 \cdot 10^{-3}$	$2/15 \cdot 10^{-3}$	400	350/500	3a	>600	>600
4	3/3.5	0.02/0.05	0.02/0.03	350	360/400	3a	>600	>600
3/3.9	2.2/3.2	0.04/0.06	0.004/0.04	300	400/500	3c	>600	>600
3	3	$6/10 \cdot 10^{-4}$	$6/10 \cdot 10^{-4}$	500	–	3b	>600	>600
7	3.7	0.005	0.005	700	380/500	3b	>600	>600
2.1	<2.1	$<2 \cdot 10^{-4}$	$<2 \cdot 10^{-4}$	500	480	3c	>600	>600
1	2.1	$<2 \cdot 10^{-4}$	$<7 \cdot 10^{-4}$	500	550	3c	>600	>600
3/2.8	2.3/2.5	$1 \cdot 10^{-3}$	$2 \cdot 10^{-2}$	500	550	3c	>600	>600
6	2.6	$8 \cdot 10^{-4}$	$5 \cdot 10^{-3}$	380	400	3c	>600	>600
8	3.4	0.01	0.03	350	400	3b	>600	>600
0	4.0	0.14	0.08	400	600	3b	>600	>600
7	3.5	0.06	0.04	300	425	3b	>600	>600
2	3.1	0.04	0.03	300	450	3b	>600	>600
0	3.0	0.03	0.04	250	350	3b	>600	>600
0	2.9	$7 \cdot 10^{-4}$	$1 \cdot 10^{-2}$	350	380	1	120/160	260/300
0	4.0	$2 \cdot 10^{-3}$	$2 \cdot 10^{-2}$	500	420	2	–	–
0	3.0	$2 \cdot 10^{-3}$	$2 \cdot 10^{-2}$	500	420	3b	420	380
6	2.6	$4 \cdot 10^{-4}$	$9 \cdot 10^{-4}$	500	450	1	300	300
1	3.0	$8 \cdot 10^{-4}$	$3 \cdot 10^{-3}$	–	425	1	175	175
1	3.2	$4 \cdot 10^{-4}$	$7 \cdot 10^{-4}$	–	595	–	–	–
9	3.7	$3 \cdot 10^{-3}$	$13 \cdot 10^{-3}$	–	350	–	–	–
5	3.5	$1 \cdot 10^{-3}$	$6 \cdot 10^{-3}$	–	400	–	–	–
14	3.10	$6 \cdot 10^{-3}$	$7 \cdot 10^{-3}$	–	430	–	–	–
	4.5	0.1	0.03	50/100	300/400	1	140/180	125/175
	7	0.04	0.3	80/150	300/400	3a	>400	>600
	8	0.06	0.03	80/150	290/300	3b	>500	>600
	5	0.04	0.02	120	250/530	3c	>600	>600
2	4	0.04	0.03	–	400	3c	>600	>600
	3.5	0.03	0.02	–	200/400	3c	>600	>600
5	3.4	$2 \cdot 10^{-3}$	$5 \cdot 10^{-3}$	–	560	1	>300	>380
5/5	3.5/5	0.001	0.01	–	300/400	3c	>300	200/600
6	3.4	0.05	0.05	–	240	3c	–	–
5	5.6	0.03	0.06	–	300/600	3a	>600	>600
8	4.0	0.12	0.07	330	–	–	–	–
	–	0.08	–	70/180	–	–	–	–
8	4.6	0.02	0.03	320	400	3a	>600	>600
2	3.7	0.01	0.03	350	400	3a	>600	>600
7	3.5	0.006	0.021	380	400	3a	>600	>600

Table II Permeability of Films Made from Various Polymers

Polymer	Temperature		Film thickness	Water vapor	N₂	Air	O₂	CO₂	H₂	Ar	He
	SI	US									
	°C	°F	μm¹)	g/cm² day	cm³/m² day bar						
PE-LD	23	73	100	1	700	1100	2000	10000	8000	–	–
PE-HD ($\rho = 0.95$ g/cm³, unstretched)	25	77	40	0.9	525	754	1890	7150	6000	–	–
	30	86	40	1.7	720	960	2270	8600	7600	–	–
	40	104	40	3.5	1220	1660	3560	13100	11400	–	–
	50	122	40	8.1	2140	2650	5650	19500	16800	–	–
PE-HD ($\rho = 0.95$ g/cm³, stretched)	25	77	40	1.0	430	680	1210	5900	5000	–	–
	30	86	40	1.6	560	830	1530	7200	6000	–	–
	40	104	40	4.3	1050	1490	2650	11200	9400	–	–
	50	122	40	10.5	1870	2670	4650	18100	14800	–	–
E/VA copolymer, VAC 20%	23	73	100	455	1400	–	4000	17000	–	–	–
Polypropylene (unstretched)	25	77	40	2.1	430	700	1900	6100	17700	1480	192
	30	86	40	3.2	600	960	2500	8400	18200	2100	217
	40	104	40	7.4	1280	1820	5100	14800	28100	4100	298
	50	122	40	19.0	2800	3600	9200	27300	46600	8000	435
Polypropylene (stretched)	25	77	40	0.81	200	350	1000	3300	6700	–	73
	30	86	40	1.2	260	480	1200	3900	8200	–	85
	40	104	40	3.3	560	940	2300	7050	12300	–	121
	50	122	40	8.4	1200	1850	4150	13200	19800	–	178
PVC-U (unstretched)	20	68	40	7.6	12	28	87	200	–⌐	–	–
PVC-U (stretched)	20	68	40	4.4	13	13	43	110	–	–	–
PVC-P	20	68	40	20	350	550	1500	8500	–	–	–
Polyvinylidenechloride	25	77	25	0.1/0.2	1.8/2.3	5/10	1.7/11	60/700	630/1400	–	–
Polystyrene (stretched)	25	77	50	14.0	27	80	235	800	1260	–	–
Polyacetal	20	68	40	2.5	10	16	50	96	420	–	–
PFEP copolymers	40	104	25	2.0	375	–	3000	6500	2000	–	–
CTFE	40	104	25	0.38/0.85	39	–	110/230	250/620	3400/5200	–	–
E/TFE copolymers	23	73	25	0.6	470	–	1560	3800	–	–	–
E/CTFE copolymers	23	73	25	9.0	150	–	39.0	1700	–	–	–
PVF	23	73	25	50.0	3.8	–	4.7	170	900	–	–
Polyamide 6	25	77	25	80/110	14	–	40	200	1500	–	–
Polyamide 66	25	77	25	15/30	11	–	80	140	–	–	–
Polyamide 11	25	77	25	1.5/4.0	50	–	540	2400	5000	–	–
Polyamide 12	25	77	25	0.35	200/280	–	800/1400	2600/5300	–	–	–
Polycarbonate	23	73	25	4	680	–	4000	14500	22000	–	–
Polyethyleneterephthalate (stretched)	23	73	25	0.6	9/15	–	80/110	200/340	1500	–	–
Polysulfone	23	73	25	6	630	–	3600	15000	28000	–	–
PU elastomers	23	73	25	13/25	550/1600	–	1000/4500	6000/22000	–	–	–
Polyimide	23	73	25	25	94	–	390	700	3800	–	–
Celluloseacetate	25	77	25	150/600	470/630	–	1800/2300	13000/15000	14000	–	–
Celluloseacetobutyrate	25	77	25	460/600	3800	–	15000	94000	–	–	–

¹) 1 μm = 0.0394 mil.

Subject Index

A

ABS 40
acrylonitrile-butadiene-styrene (ABS) 14
addition polymerization 7, 167
additives 15
air ring 146
alternating 14
amorphous thermoplastic 11
annual polymer production 3
antistatic agents 16
approach or land 82

B

Bagley 62
banbury mixer, 105
barrier flights 79
biaxial molecular orientation 151
biaxial stretching 145
bipolymer 14
block 14
blow molding 148
blowing agents 17
branching 10
break up time 103
Brinkman number, Br 52

C

calendering 159
capillary number 102
capillary visco-meter 60
carbon black 99
cast film extrusion 143
Castro-Macosko curing model 170
cavity transfer mixing section 107
check valve 127
chemical foaming 175
clamping force 122
clamping unit 127
closed discharge 72
co-injection molding 131
co-rotating twin screw extruder 111
coat-hanger sheeting die 82
cokneader 110
collapsing rolls 146
compression molding 171
computer simulation 132
condensation polymerization 9, 167
cone-and-plate rheometer 63
consistency index 49
continuity equation 207
cooling system 128
cooling time 119
copolymers 14
Couette flow 51
counter-rotating twin screw extruder 112

CRD mixing section 108
creep rupture 29
creep test 26
critical capillary number 102
cross-head tubing die 84
cross-linking 13
crosslinked elastomers 13
curing reaction models169
curing thermoset 56
curtain coating 163

D

Deborah number 54
degradation 120
degree of cure 56
die lips 82
differential scanning calorimeter (DSC) 168
dioctylphthalate 15
dip coating 163
disperive static mixer 110
dispersed melting 110
dispersive mixing 99
distributive mixing 95
drop break-up 103
dynamic fatigue. 39
dynamic mechanical tests 29

E

ejector system 128
elastic shear modulus 32
energy equation 207
equation of motion 208
Erwin's ideal mixer 99
ethylene 8
extrudate swell 53
extrudate swell 54
extruder dimensions 70
extrusion blow molding 149
extrusion die 82

F

fatigue 39
fiber orientation 132, 172
fiber reinforced polymer (FRP) 32
fiber spinning 141
filled polymers 25
fillers 16
film blowing 145
flash 120
flex lips 82
flow number 101
foaming 175
forward roll coating164
freezing line 145

G

gate 128
glass mat reinforced thermoplastic 171
glass transition temperature 11, 13
graft copolymers 14
grooved feed extruders 73
grooved feed section 73

H

Hagen-Poiseuille flow 50
Halpin and Tsai 34
Hele–Shaw model 132
high impact polystyrene (PS-HI) 14
hydraulic clamping unit 128

I

impact strength 36
injection blow molding 151
injection molding 117, 132
injection molding cycle 118
injection molding machine 117
injection pressure 122
internal batch mixer. 105
isochronous 27
isometric creep plots 27

K

Kenics static mixer 109
knife coating 163

L

lamellar crystal 12
laminar mixing 95
LDPE 48, 53
long fiber composites 33
loss modulus 32
loss tangent 32
low density polyethylene 115

M

Maddock 108
manifold 82
mechanical properties 19
melt film 76
melt flow indexer 60
melt fracture 54
melt pool 76
melting or transition zone 76
melting temperature. 13
metering zone 80
mixing devices 104
mold cavity 128
molding diagram 120
molecular weight 9
morphology development 111

morphology development in polymer blends 95
multi-color injection molding 131
multi-component injection molding 131

N

Newtonian plateau 48
nitrogen compounds 16
non-isothermal flows 52
normal stress coefficients 52
normal Stresses 52
nozzle 127
nucleating agents 17

O

open discharge. 72
optimal orientation 99

P

parison 149
parison programming 149
particulate solid agglomerates 99
Paul Troester Maschinenfabrik 67
phenol-formaldehyde 13
phenolic 13
physical foaming 175
pin barrel extruder 107
pin mixing section 106
pinch-off 152
pineapple mixing section 107
plasticating single screw extruder 69
plasticating unit 126
plasticizers 15
plug-assist thermoforming 153
polyamide 9
polyethylene 8, 207
polyisobutylene 19
polypropylene 30, 113
polypropylene copolymer 26
polystyrene 114
power law index. 49
power-law model 48
pressure flow 50
properties 6
pumping systems 67
pvT diagram 120

Q

QSM-extruder 106

R

random 14
reactive polymers 167
reduced first normal stress difference 53
reduced viscosity 48
reinforced polymers 32
residual stress 125, 174

reverse draw thermoforming 153
rheology 47
rheology of curing chermosets 56
ribbing in roll coating165
roll coating 163
rotational molding 176
rubber 1
rubber compound 99
rubber elasticity 24

S
S-N curves 39
scaling 181
screen pack, 141
screw characterisctic curves 71
self-cleaning 111
semi-crystalline thermoplastic 12
shark skin 54
shear thinning behavior 48
sheet molding compound 171
sheeting die 82
short fiber composites 33
short shot 120
short-term tensile test 22
shrinkage 174
simple shear flow 49
simplified flows 49
single screw extruder 68
sink marks 125
sinusoidal oscillatory test 31
slide coating 163
sliding plate rheometer 47
smooth barrel 71
solid bed 76
solids conveying zone 72
song of Deborah 55
sperulitic structure 12
spider die 84
spinneret 141
spiral die 85
sprue and runner system 128
spurt flow 54
stability analysis of spinning 142
stability analysis of film casting 143
stabilizers 16
static fatigue 38
stick-slip 54
storage modulus 32
stress relaxation 19
structure of polymers 7
stuffing machine 117
styrene-butadiene-rubber (SBR) 14
suspension rheology 57

T
Tadmor model 78
terpolymer 14
thermal fatigue. 40

thermoforming 152
thermosets 13
time-temperature superposition 20
toggle mechanism 127
tubular die 84
twin screw extruders 69, 111

U
U.S. polymer production 4
Union Carbide mixing section 108
unsaturated 35
unsaturated polyester 168
upper bound 99

V
vinyl ester 56
viscoelastic flow models 58
viscoelasticity 19
viscosity curves 114
viscous heating 52
volume-specific energy to fracture 37

W
warpage 125, 174
weathering 40
Weissenberg–Rabinowitsch equation 62
wind-up station 159
wire coating 163
WLF equation 21

Tim A. Osswald is an Associate Professor of Mechanical Engineering and Director of the Polymer Processing Research Group at the University of Wisconsin-Madison. Originally from Cúcuta, Colombia, he received his B.S. and M.S. in Mechanical Engineering from the South Dakota School of Mines and Technology and his Ph.D. in Mechanical Engineering at the University of Illinois at Urbana-Champaign in the field of Polymer Processing. He spent two and one half years at the Institute for Plastics Processing (IKV) in Aachen, Germany, as an Alexander von Humboldt Fellow. In 1991, he received the National Science Foundation's Presidential Young Investigator Award. Currently, he teaches polymer processing and designing with polymers and his research projects include: mixing, extrusion, compression molding, thermomechanical behavior of fiber reinforced parts, boundary element simulation of the non-isothermal, non-Newtonian flow of polymer melts. In addition to this book, Professor Osswald has published over 100 papers, the book *Materials Science of Polymers for Engineers* (Hanser, 1996), and has contributed many book chapters. Professor Osswald has also been consulted by several industries and is one of the co-founders of The Madison Group - Polymer Processing Research Corporation.